Making Traditional Wooden Planes

John M. Whelan

Illustrated by the Author

The Astragal Press
Mendham, New Jersey

Photographs by Unique Photography Studio
Ledgewood, New Jersey

Library of Congress Catalog Card Number: 96-83120
International Standard Book Number: 1-879335-69-7

Published by
THE ASTRAGAL PRESS
5 Cold Hill Road, Suite 12
P.O. Box 239
Mendham, New Jersey 07945-0239

Dedicated to Emil Pollak,
a giant not only in tool history but as a human being.

ACKNOWLEDGEMENTS

The concept for this work was formulated by Emil Pollak, and it was at his instigation that it was attempted. The book design was by Martyl Pollak, who also arranged for its production. Both have been enormously helpful.

The book was greatly improved in readability and accuracy by the editorial talents of Herbert Kean, who is still my friend, even after I rejected some of his suggestions. Blame me for any remaining errors.

My education in plane matters owes much to the knowledgeable members of the various tool organizations. In particular, the New Jersey tool club, CRAFTS, has taught me much. One member in particular, Frank Lemoine, improved the appearance of many of these planes by his generous gift of a hoard of well-seasoned applewood.

My most patient wife, Helen, not only acquiesced in the launching of a second book after tolerating four years of my irascibility during the gestation of my first, but assisted in the onerous proof-reading. Greater love hath no woman!

TABLE OF CONTENTS

WHY MAKE A WOODEN PLANE? This tool, long considered obsolete, is enjoying a resurgence of interest. It is being rediscovered by those who enjoy working wood with hand tools. They learn that the wooden planes offer performance at least equal to the metal varieties, and that they offer the user a more pleasurable intimacy with the wood. There is a challenge in learning the art of tuning the tool to give peak performance, and its mastery brings gratification.

In recent years, we have seen a growing population of amateur woodworkers having the time and ability to do first-rate work. Appreciation of the wooden plane has grown to the point that professional makers are appearing once again, not only in Europe but in this country. Their products command high prices, well above the equivalent metal tools.

If you are a woodworker, you know the satisfaction of creating something with your own hands that you recognize as useful and good. The pride you had in the first birdhouse you built as a child has been recaptured over and again. Even if you have not experienced the pleasure of using a well-tuned wooden plane, you will enjoy making one. To create a tool that works to your satisfaction will bring a feeling of accomplishment, not only when you first admire its appearance and smooth performance, but for many years afterward as you use it.

You will use it. The metal planes drove the wooden ones from the marketplace because they could be adjusted more rapidly, required less maintenance and could be used even by inexperienced workers. But the wooden ones remained in use by those with the skill to use them, even if their only source was their own workshop. At the tool meets, auctions and flea markets you will find many well-made planes without the name stamp of a professional maker. I suspect that some of these were made because they couldn't be found in the marketplace. The skilled workers who made them recognized their superiority, and would not settle for the available metal planes.

It is questionable whether the professional woodworker can justify, on the economic level, the time and facility use required to make his own planes (unless one is required that is not otherwise obtainable). Even the highly skilled will encounter unfamiliar operations and tools, and time estimates for the task have a way of proving to have been quite low. But many professionals do make planes, for the same reasons we do.

Wooden planes provide the principal focus for many tool collectors. They are discovering that the enormous variety available in the antique marketplace not only challenges their hunting spirit, but offers insight into the creativity and craftsmanship of earlier generations. If your interest is primarily in collecting, you will want to learn more about your planes. Unless you are unusually perceptive and have spent much time scrutinizing them, there are many details of their architecture which remain for your discovery. Using a good prototype and following its design closely as you try to reproduce it will disclose niceties you were unaware of. Your knowledge of the art of plane design will increase. You will have an enhanced appreciation of the generations of tradesmen who earned their living by using planes and who applied their ingenuity to making these tools easier to use and more productive.

This will be true if you attempt to follow faithfully the procedures the early makers used, without any power other than that of their bodies. It will be equally true if you choose to copy the late nineteenth century workers who used machines to accomplish those operations which can be done faster and more accurately by use of power. The early makers spent years in apprenticeship. They acquired an effortless ability to saw precisely on the line, and pare a surface truly flat with chisels; and to do this rapidly. Amateurs without their high level of hand tool proficiency cannot do this, but must rely on power tools and jigs when possible, and slow, painstaking progress when the task cannot be adapted to these.

Once you have produced a useful working tool, your feeling for the abilities of the old planemakers will be vastly improved. You will accomplish more than this, however. You will have become a better woodworker.

LEARNING HOW   In spite of a number of well-written articles on making wooden planes, the beginner will often encounter problems not covered. My first plane (as you will learn later) was a disappointment, although I had the fine instructions available in the work by Perch and Lee (1981).

It appeared that a description by an amateur, rather than a professional woodworker, might be useful. Although I had made a dozen or so planes before (mostly historic replicas), this book began by making all of the planes described herein, keeping a record of difficulties encountered and how they were overcome. No amount of close study of this text, however, will teach you how to make a working plane. You must make one.

You will learn that there is much difference between making a wooden plane for display, and one which is intended to be used. If the former is your objective, your task will be easier. Your products will be fully as attractive as the working tools, and, indeed, indistinguishable from them by all except wooden plane users. The replicas mentioned above and shown in the photograph on p.117 were intended only for visualization of their appearance, and are in no sense of the word usable. If your intention is to make working tools and your only prior experience with them is with antique tools you have restored yourself, you are at risk of concluding that the wooden planes aren't as satisfactory as the commercial metal ones. Please, do not do so until you have had the opportunity to use a well-made and finely tuned example.

TOOL REQUIREMENTS   The early planemakers had a wide variety of specialized tools for their trade. The bulk of these were jigs or holding fixtures, or special planes designed for just one operation. They were developed to expedite rapid production of many planes, and were very effective for this purpose. You will find pictures and descriptions of these production-type aids in references cited in Chapter 2. You will not need them unless your objective is to go into production. Aside from good saws, planes, chisels, measuring and other common tools, there are two essential requirements for planemaking (unless you are satisfied with simple kit assembly). One is a woodworker's bench with adequate vise facilities for holding the work. One cannot cut a proper opening in the plane body for its cutter while holding the body with one hand. The other is a set of sharpening stones and the ability to use them to produce a truly keen edge.

The early planemakers had no power tools. All of their specialized tools were made either in their own shops or by a nearby blacksmith. Today, there are apartment dwellers who make beautiful planes without power tools of any kind. If you have the necessary woodworking ability with hand tools, this imposes no limitation and offers great pleasure. With limited hand tool proficiency, power tools facilitate many (not all) of the required operations.

The planes described in this book were made by the author in his typical home workshop, neither the fully equipped dream shop of a tool retailer's display, nor a do-it-yourselfer's garage. The existing tools were used, except for those made for the purpose in the same shop. Although the descriptions are written in the present tense and in general terms to provide better readability in your shop, they describe exactly the procedures used in making the tools pictured.

You will learn more, however, if the instructions are not followed too closely. By all means, buy or borrow an authentic wooden plane of the type you plan to make. Study it, and use it as a prototype. Decide which features you wish to duplicate exactly, and which you prefer to change. Your personal preferences should govern in details of ornamentation, choice of materials and some aspects of design. As you will see in the individual descriptions, the planes chosen as prototypes were not exactly duplicated. Where deviations were made, however, they have been noted and reasons (even if only personal idiosyncrasies) given.

Simplification of some of the more elaborate, purely decorative features of your prototype will save much effort and some frustration, if a simpler pattern will satisfy you. Remember that the old makers had available specialized molding planes which enabled them to produce such features quickly and accurately. Be aware, however, that the design of the functional parts of your prototypes has been honed by generations of users. Change these only if you are prepared to treat such changes as experimental, and if need be, to accept a realization that the old timers knew best, after all.

Aside from design considerations, do not accept the methodology described here as the best for you and your shop. The use of the metalworker's end mills, for example, has only recently become popular in wood shops (see, for example, Beck, 1993, in the bibliography). They proved to be very useful for certain operations, such as inlays for metal components, when used in combination with a drill press cross vise. You may find other techniques, (hand or power routers, for instance) useful in your hands and with your equipment. The descriptions should make clear what must be accomplished, and the way I chose to go about doing it; they will suggest alternative approaches.

The making of plane irons and metal hardware described herein requires certain metal-working facilities. However, alternate sources are suggested for these items if you prefer to restrict your fabrication to wood.

The risk of alienating experienced woodworkers has been accepted by giving detail that they all know and do not need. I would rather force them to skip a paragraph, than omit a detail or precautions that one less experienced would welcome. You all know about "measure twice, cut once". Before you finish a plane, you will have invested some fine wood of a size not readily found, and much time. In such cases, not only measure twice, but make quite sure you are measuring what you think you are measuring. For critical operations on a machine setup, it is good insurance to make a trial cut on scrap wood. There have been occasions when I sincerely regretted not having done so!

SAFETY   If you are serious about working wood, you have been warned in almost all of the publications devoted to the subject about the hazards involved. If woodworking is new to you, take the time to familiarize yourself with the safety precautions in your tool manuals. Some of the operations described herein can cause injury if treated too casually. As simple a thing as a chisel can cause injury. If one drops, do not try to catch it! A power tool can do even more damage.

Inattention and haste are behind most injuries. If at any time the thought strikes you that "I shouldn't be doing it this way"—STOP! Take the time to do it the safe way. It will usually be the best way to accomplish what it is you are trying to do.

You are working wood because you enjoy doing so. Undue eagerness to complete a task detracts from the enjoyment of it. A hasty cut that destroys much earlier effort is very painful. One that injures you is much more so. Think through every operation. It is much easier to work wood with a full complement of fingers.

In making a plane, the production of the finished tool should not be the sole satisfaction. Remember that the pleasure of a voyage should be in the trip as well as in the destination. Savor the making, and do not be in too much haste to finish it.

CHAPTER 1

THE CHARACTERISTICS OF A GOOD PLANE

If your plane is to perform satisfactorily, there are certain essential conditions that must be met, and others which are very desirable. Some of these are not readily apparent on casual examination of the prototype tool. Such requirements should really be stressed for each of the planes to be described, but this would be boring repetition. Let's discuss them here, and simply refer to sections of this chapter in the later ones. Reference to Fig. 2:1 should make clear the location of plane parts whose names you do not recognize.

MATERIAL   The body (stock) of a wooden plane must be hard and wear resistant. A plane made of a soft wood such as pine might serve for a one-time job in a pinch, but will otherwise not repay the effort of making it (unless you make it as a practice run before starting with a less available wood).

The stock must be resistant to changes in size or shape. Any warping or bowing that affects the shape of its bottom (sole) will cause poor performance indeed. For this reason planemakers were quite particular about choosing stable, well-dried wood for their products. Most early planes predate the extensive availability of kiln dried wood. (Some modern workers regard this as having been a blessing, as they feel that air dried wood is preferable.) Hardwoods today (except for some tropical species) are normally kiln dried. However the moisture is removed, your material should be allowed to equilibrate with the humidity conditions of your shop for a month or more before cutting to a final shape. This stabilizes the moisture content, and allows the wood to settle down dimensionally before you start to work it.

Except for the yellow birch planes of the early New England planemakers, by far the largest number of American and English planes were made of beechwood. Air dried stock was the norm in early times, and one year of air drying per inch of thickness was

considered a bare minimum. At least one large producer steamed the beech logs to loosen bark and drive out sap, and followed this with bark removal and four years of air drying. The logs were then roughly cut into the sizes required for the various planes, and enough of these blanks to supply the factory for several years were stored in air drying sheds.

Some early makers selected their dried plane blanks well in advance and immersed them in linseed oil until needed. While this may have given better penetration than surface oiling and perhaps lubricated the chisels during the necessary cutting operations, it is a bit messy and the practice did not survive.

While beechwood was the workhorse of the planemaking trade, premium planes were offered in other woods as well in the catalogs of the large suppliers. The next step up was applewood, and top of the line was boxwood, rosewood or ebony. Maple, in my opinion a fine tool wood, was rarely used except by craftsmen making their own tools. Mahogany (except for the now almost unobtainable Cuban variety) is a bit soft for plane use, but will serve for a plane not in daily use. Lignum vitae and some other tropical woods perform well, and add an attractive appearance to good service.

Today's casual planemaker will find, in many parts of the country, that suitable hardwood of the required thickness is not easily found. Lumber suppliers prefer to handle one inch thick material, which requires less time in their drying kilns to reach acceptable moisture levels. Even when three-inch (or twelve-quarter, as dealers call it) thicknesses of a suitable hardwood are available, it may not include the quarter-sawn stock you should prefer. Telephone prospecting of lumber dealers in the Middle Atlantic states produced only stocks of maple and mahogany in the required size; small amounts of boxwood and ebony were found further afield. Suppliers' inventories change with time, and you may have better luck.

I was fortunate in acquiring a center plank of beech from a log privately sawn and well air dried. My supply of applewood, a most rewarding material to work, was from a hoard stored for many years by a woodworking friend. Finding suitable material for your plane is your first task.

GRAIN   Straight grain greatly simplifies the planemaker's task and is very desirable. Although you will occasionally find an old professionally made plane with a tight knot or other defect in its stock, most of these have survived without warping. This is a tribute to the maker's familiarity with his material, his ability to predict which defects would not interfere with plane performance. Without his experience, we learners are best advised to use only defect free lumber.

Attention must be given to the orientation of the grain of the wood in the stock blank. Almost all old bench planes (smooth, jack, jointer etc.) will show a pattern of tree growth rings on their toe and heel that run nearly horizontally. They will all have the growth rings curving downward toward the sole, as sketched in Fig.1:1. The way to provide this characteristic is to use only quarter-sawn stock, ideally from the center plank of the tree.

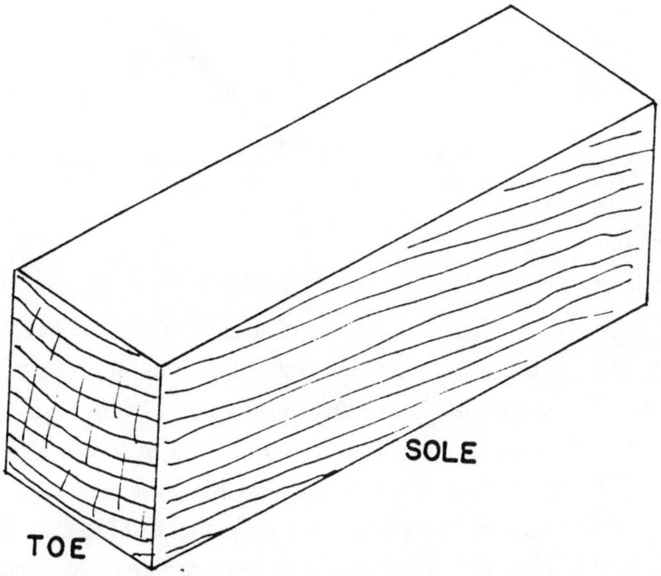

Planemakers commonly believed that the wood nearest the bark of the tree was the hardest. Although modern tests do not find a difference, it is probably true that generations of experience taught the old makers that plane soles wore better if they were cut in this way. Saying "harder" might have been their way of expressing this observation. Noting which face of the blank was nearest to the bark while it was in the tree, and choosing this as the plane sole, produces the observed growth ring orientation. The same choice is noted in the most common molders, the hollows and rounds. Other molders, and other types including plow planes, may be found in other orientations.

It may be argued that vertical growth ring orientation is better, as dimensional change in the width of the stock with changes in moisture content is less in this case. I am content to rely on the preference of the old professionals for horizontal growth rings, as testified almost universally by their bench planes.

While perfectly flat grain (in which the wood fibers run parallel to the sole) is ideal, this is seldom found in the real world. As you know, wood prefers to be planed in the direction in which its wood fibers slope upward as the plane moves forward. If you do not cater to this preference, the wood responds by producing a rough surface or tear-out. If you hand plane the sole of your body blank, you will select the preferred planing direction. This should become the toe-to-heel direction of your plane. To say this another way, the toe of the plane should show the outermost growth ring observable in the stock. This choice for the toe means that, in use, the fibers of the plane sole slope downward from toe to heel, as seen in Fig. 1:1. The possibility of having the sole catch on a defect in the surface being planed is reduced, and with it the risk of marring the sole.

The proper grain orientation in the material to be used is not as critical as

Figure 1:1

some of the other conditions described here. Useful planes can be made even if the grain preference cannot be satisfied. Some of my earlier planes stretch these requirements, and still work well. If your search for suitable wood is unsuccessful, do not let failure to achieve the desired grain orientation keep you from making a plane. However, the importance that the early planemakers attached to it, as indicated by observing the grain in the great majority of their planes, suggests that finding wood which will allow you to copy their practice is worth the hunt.

SQUARING   Having obtained your wood and decided how the plane body is to be oriented, the body blank is cut out. Whether done by hand or machine, pains must be taken to ensure that all corners are accurately square, that top and bottom are parallel and at right angles to the sides and to the front and back. The planemaker simply says "the blank is squared". If you prefer to avoid the use of power tools, achieving this objective with hand planes will test your ability as a woodworker. Lack of accuracy in this task will cause no end of problems in laying out the cuts to be made, and in subsequent cutting. One early worker flatly stated that "a stock improperly squared is useless".

MOUTH   When a knife or chisel cuts along the grain of wood, there is a tendency for the cut to propagate in front of the cutting edge as a split, a separation of the wood fibers. This is not too important as long as the shaving removed is thin and bends readily. A thicker shaving climbs the face of the cutting tool, and tends to be pried up and generate splits in the wood ahead of the cutting edge. This splitting gives a rougher surface than cutting does. The function of the plane body is to permit taking a thicker shaving by cutting, rather than splitting. Its most important task is to apply pressure on the wood surface immediately in front of the cutting edge. This presses down on the part that is being forced upward by the shaving, and combats the tendency to split ahead of the edge. Fig. 1:2 (the cutting blades in black) illustrates a heavy chisel cut in the top sketch,

and a cut of the same depth by a plane in the lower one.

The slit in the sole through which the cutting edge of the plane blade peeks is called the mouth of the plane. Obviously, the nearer the front of this slit is to the cutting edge (the smaller the mouth opening), the more effective it is in preventing splitting. The limitation, of course, is that the mouth must allow the passage of the thickest shaving to be taken. Metal planes, and the so-called "reform" wooden planes, allow for adjustment of the clearance for the shaving by either moving the blade support (metal planes) or a segment of the sole (reform planes). The early woodworkers had another solution. They kept more than one smooth plane, with different mouth openings. The plane used for the final finish (the German name for this tool may be translated as "polishing plane") has a mouth only large enough to pass a very fine shaving.

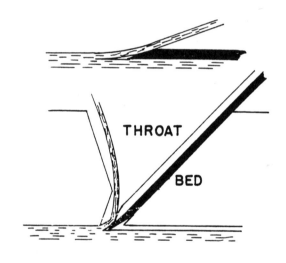

Figure 1:2

This requirement of a narrow gap between the cutting edge and the front of the mouth is one of the more difficult to meet in making a plane. It is very easy to overcut your layout lines in the process of flattening the blade bed, and this is the most common flaw in first planes. A jack plane, used to take deep cuts and requiring a more open mouth than a smooth plane, might be a good first project. Plan your work to make the mouth opening small. It is much easier

6

to expand it than to shrink it.

Another important aid in controlling splitting in front of the cutting edge is the cap iron. This serves to break the shaving before it can climb the face of the iron far enough to develop leverage and cause splitting. The lower sketch of Fig.1:2 shows the shaving being broken by the cap iron.

It is not enough simply to have a small mouth opening. If the sole is not flat, the portion of the sole in front of the blade may not touch the workpiece and thus cannot perform its function of pressing down on it. The final flattening of the sole is an important step in finishing any bench plane. The procedure for doing this is covered on page 15.

BLADE MOUNTING   Another very important factor in plane performance is holding the cutting edge rigidly in position. There are a number of ways of accomplishing this, but all must guarantee that the lower end of the blade is held so tightly that it cannot vibrate under the stress of use. If it does, the blade will "chatter" and produce corrugations or ridges across the width of the cut. The need to allow room for the shavings to escape means that the wedge or other holding device cannot press on the cutter too close to the cutting edge. The design of the mounting must be such that the heaviest pressure on the cutter is exerted as near to the cutting edge as possible. The bed, the surface which supports the back of the cutter, must have no projections which prevent this. It must be flat (or very slightly hollow) so that the full width of the cutting edge is supported. Any irregularity in the bed which prevents either side of the cutting edge from receiving sturdy support must be corrected. The wedge must be fitted to the plane carefully, to assure that it bears most heavily on the lower end of the cutter.

THROAT FRONT   The passage through the stock in front of the cutter (the throat) should offer no obstacle to the passage of shavings. Even the best design will occasionally "choke", filling this escape path with packed curls of wood and preventing further cutting. The "eyes" of the plane (seen in Fig. 2:1) are there to make it more comfortable for fingers entering the throat to remove shavings. A careful worker does this often, not waiting until a choke occurs.

A plane that chokes too often is a frustrating tool. Some remedies for this are covered in Chapter 3. An obstacle in the throat (such as the core pin of Chapter 4) may restrict the use of the tool to light cuts unless it is carefully planned.

Were shavings clearance the only consideration, the throat would be made as open as possible (as in metal planes). Because wooden bench planes are subject to much more rapid sole wear and scarring than metal planes are, they are designed to allow for periodic dressing of the sole by planing. As wood is removed from the sole, the mouth opening will widen unless the throat front slopes backward at the same angle as the cutter. However, this would allow only a narrow shavings passage and would be subject to shavings hangup and choking. The classic design (seen in the lower sketch of Fig. 1:2) slopes the lower throat front backward (toward the heel) at an angle which is a compromise between the conflicting requirements of preventing choking and maintaining the proper mouth opening as the sole wears. This backward slope continues for a short distance, beyond the expected loss of sole. The throat front then breaks to a forward slope for easier shavings exit and to allow easier access for the fingers trying to clear a choke. Further details of the classic throat design are given in Chapter 6.

CHAPTER 2

HOW THE OLD PLANES WERE MADE

Contemporaneous accounts of the style and use of the wooden plane are scarce enough, but accounts of how they were made are almost nonexistent. Those few contemporaries who wrote about the woodworking crafts were primarily interested in describing the tools and how they were used, rather than how they were made. To learn how the earliest makers proceeded, we must for the most part read from their works in wood, not on paper.

Before the end of the eighteenth century, professional planemaking was largely accomplished in small shops, by the master and at most a few apprentices and journeymen. There was little specialization. The workers made whatever type of plane was required for orders or for stock. To be sure, the master was more likely to make the more difficult planes, such as plows and filletsters. Perhaps he was the only one trusted to do the more difficult tasks such as the intricate dovetail fitting required for installing the wear resistant boxwood implants.

These enterprises supplied only a local market, no larger than one that could be reached by horse-drawn wagon transport. This pattern was forced to change in the America of the first half of the nineteenth century, as demand for woodworking tools expanded. Larger shops employed a number of planemakers, and specialization began. The tools and methods did not change much initially, and some of

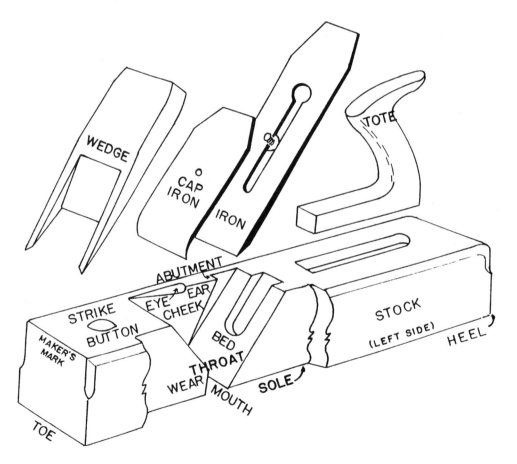

Figure 2:1

8

the tools in the kits of workers of this period are probably representative of those used by the earliest professionals.

With piece work providing a strong incentive to speed each step, the planemakers designed and made implements to do this (long before "time and motion study" became the rage). Simple patterns or templates were made which removed the need for measurement in layout. The proper guide was simply laid against the stock and the layout line was scribed. Fixtures for holding the plane bodies during the several operations were developed, saving the time needed to readjust the bench vice. Such specialized gadgets are useful only if you make many copies of the same plane, so that they will get no more than a brief mention here.

WILDUNG COLLECTION

A glimpse into the methods used is offered by several collections of planemaker's tools which have survived. One of these, 41 tools amassed by a planemaker who began his career with the Sandusky Tool Co. in 1882, is now in the Wildung collection of the Shelburne Museum in Vermont. Photographs of these, and pictures of their use in the several stages of making a jack plane, accompany an article (Wildung 1955) describing this sequence of steps as performed in the days before mechanization. The same sequence is described by a number of other workers, and is undoubtedly the preferred method if power tools are not used. The block is squared. After laying out locations of mouth and throat, the mouth is drilled with a $\frac{1}{8}$" bit. The stock is turned over, and holes are bored in the top to remove waste wood between the bed and the front of the throat. (Some chisel the throat before drilling the mouth.) The rest of the waste is chiseled away, making sure that the bed is perfectly flat by using a heavy, wide "bedding" chisel. Clean up the mouth of the plane and cut the wedge abutments. These are made perfectly even with floats (tools described later on p. 61). The cheeks (sides of the throat) are cut with "cheeking" chisels (broad skew chisels). The account continues with the finishing steps essentially as covered in the descriptions of our later chapters. It con-

cludes with "Making a plane by hand requires much care and skill."

OTHER COLLECTIONS

Kenneth Roberts Volume II (1983) contains much further information on hand planemaking. The tool kit of Alfred Tovey, who worked in the Doscher Plane Co. around the turn of the twentieth century, is described. Photographs show his chisels, gouges and floats, as well as a number of wooden templates and the fixtures used to hold the stocks during the several operations. There are also photographs of a portion of the Woolcott collection of "backing" or "mother" planes, used to form the sole profiles of molding planes. The collection is preserved by Colonial Williamsburg.

In this same volume, Mr. Edward Ingraham describes his methods for reproduction of eighteenth century molding planes, copying the hand methods by which they were made originally. The procedures given here later parallel these, as adapted for power tool use.

BRITISH

An admirable summary of available information on British planemaking is given by Jane and Mark Rees (Rees 1993). The recollections of one of the planemakers employed by Charles Nurse and Co. in the 1920's include a workday of eleven hours, with half-days on Saturdays, for the staff of six. They were paid at piecework rates.

Small scale manufacture of wooden planes by hand continued in England until the second half of the twentieth century. A photograph of the planemaking shop of Wm. Marples & Sons in their 1909 catalog (reprinted in Rees) shows ten men at work at individual benches. Marples continued this operation into the 1960's. At that time, the staff was divided only into "bench" hands (who made the bench planes) and those who made all other types. All hands furnished their own tools and fixtures, save for the molding plane makers who used the firm's "mother" planes to shape the patterned sole.

The Rees volume contains photographs of several stages in the formation of both a jack and a molding plane, and a number of the tools and jigs that

9

the Marples workers used. Shortly before this shop was closed, some of these last few professionals who made planes by hand were interviewed by Ken Hawley. He arranged for one of them to make a cinematographic record of the process, an invaluable document recording a skill which you and I are trying to relearn. The paring of the bed of a bench plane to form a true flat surface is seen as requiring much physical effort. The driving force for the "bedding" chisel was the shoulder. The worker stated that it took a week after returning from holiday to "get his shoulder back in shape", and in the interim it became badly bruised. The speed with which he formed a flat bed will amaze you if you see the film after having done the same job yourself.

COMMERCIAL PRODUCTION   By the middle of the nineteenth century, increased demand and increased means of commercial transportation changed the pattern of planemaking. Workshops became larger, with benches for a dozen or more workers. These planemakers made only one type of plane. A usual division was into bench, molding, and "stop work", that is, plows, filletsters and grooving planes. Hermon Chapin had work agreements with sixteen planemakers in 1837, and led the transition to larger scale production.

The more efficient planemakers expanded and sought faster and more economical means of production. In the United States, specialization was carried much further as the demand for planes grew faster than the supply of skilled plane makers. Machines were designed and made to accomplish, wherever possible, individual steps in the process and operators (even prison inmates) were trained to use these. Workshops expanded into factories with machine tools driven by water power.

The Sandusky Tool Co. at the turn of the twentieth century reduced handwork as much as was possible at that time. According to an account by William Lorenzen, an official of the company at that time, they had 36 planemaker's benches. These produced a maximum of 1200 planes a day (Wildung 1955). No matter how much was done by machines,

it is hard to believe that a plane could be finished in only eighteen minutes of bench work, as required by these figures. The average rate of production from the financial figures of the company (Roberts 1978 p.234) was at most about 70,000 planes per year or about seven planes per bench per workday. Even this will appear unbelievable after you have made a plane. But then, you will not have had the machine work done for you.

The bench plane stocks were cut to length on a twin saw and planed on two sides at once by a twin machine planer, turned and planed square top and bottom. The beginning of the throat and bed was machine cut with a "beater", then the mouth and cheeks were cut by another machine. The bed was pared by machine, another machine cut the "eyes". The nearly complete stock was turned over to the "fitter" to fit the wedges and irons (the irons being from another department), who could accomplish this (on piecework) at a rate of 200 per day. (One every three minutes!) The "finisher" then applied the finishing touches (I presume this meant the chamfers, etc.) at the same rate of production. They went to the inspector, then were finished with linseed oil before they reached the packing room.

Molding planes required more hand work, although not nearly as much as we go through. Their stocks were cut and planed to size by machine, and the sole was profiled by a molding machine called a "sticker". They were then turned over to a "finisher" who cut the wedge mortise, fitted the iron, and used a drum sander to complete the body trimming. In contrast to the bench plane irons, which were available from stock ready for use, the molding plane irons were supplied unprofiled and not hardened. Hollows, rounds, and beads had their cutting edges scribed using a template. Every other type of molding plane had its iron individually inserted into its mortise and scribed to conform to the shape of its sole. The profile of the iron was roughly shaped in a punch press, then ground to its final shape and beveled. It was sent to another department to be hardened and tempered. The Roman numerals often seen on the shanks of molding plane irons were put there to ensure that the iron reached its own plane (which had been correspondingly marked in pencil) on return from this process.

Although not spelled out in the account cited, the procedure for making molding plane wedges was to cut the finial for a dozen or more at a time using special planes.

A more detailed description of the making of planes was presented by W.J. Armour in a magazine series in 1898. This has been reprinted (Roberts 1983); it is the best contemporaneous account that I am aware of. It is too lengthy to reprint here, but much of his description is recapitulated piecemeal herein. Armour was a planemaker who worked in London from 1874 into the early twentieth century. His marks include "FROM JOHN MOSELEY & SON" (later "& SONS"), suggesting his familiarity with their operations.

His description of the making of a molding plane deserves at least a brief review. Some of his specific measurements may have been the standard at Moseley, but examination of the molders of other producers shows that they were not universally accepted. The names of the molder features are shown in Fig. 2:2.

He squares the block of beech for the stock, and cuts back the top of the stock for the handhold at this point. The bed line marking the support surface for the iron is scribed on the sole $3\frac{1}{2}$" from the toe, the mouth line $\frac{3}{16}$" forward of this. The bed line is carried up both sides of the plane at the chosen pitch; 50° for joiners, about 60° for cabinetmakers. These

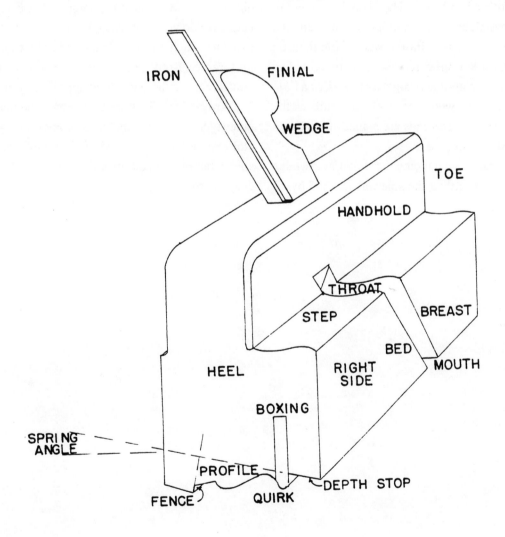

Figure 2:2

11

lines are joined by one across the top of the stock. Mark a line for the front of the wedge mortise one inch forward of this. Lines now join this one to the mouth line on the sole, down both sides of the stock.

The outline of the top of the wedge mortise is completed by marking for its sides, making its width one-third of the width of the handhold. The left edge of the sole profile is placed at the same distance from the side as the left side of the wedge mortise. The mouth is sawn in along the bed and front lines down to the left side of the profile on the sole and to the handhold. The wood between these saw cuts is removed with thin chisels. A hole is bored from the center of the wedge mortise outline on top of the stock to the center of the mouth, and the wedge mortise is cut out with saw float and a square float. The sole profile is then cut. The blank iron is put in place, the mouth being pared to just admit it, and the wedge mortise finished. Fit the wedge, file the iron to match the sole profile, harden and temper it. The face of the iron is ground straight and the back a little hollow. Plane the wedge to apply pressure at the bottom of the iron. The ends are planed smooth and the stock edges trimmed.

The sequence which cuts the throat and wedge mortise before profiling the sole was favored by all of the old professional planemakers of which I have details. As they cut the mortise by hand, their heavy mortise chisel work would have risked damage to a preformed sole profile. They had well maintained "mother" planes to cut the sole, which minimized risk of damage to the mouth during profiling (a mother plane is a molding plane with a sole cut as a negative copy of the sole needed in the plane being made).

I prefer the sequence used by Edward Ingraham in duplicating early New England planes (Roberts 1983); he profiles the sole before the mortise is cut. Without a mother plane, finishing the sole profile requires using a scraper to finish the profile, and this is easier without the mouth opening to worry about. Using machine help in sinking the mortise decreases the amount of mallet work needed, and lessens the danger of sole damage (although great care is still needed). However, if you plan to make a molding plane to match an existing iron, the older method is preferable. Both sequences have good and bad points; choose the one which appeals to you.

Armour's series goes on to cover the making of other types of plane, and is recommended as collateral reading. You will find the same information in somewhat more detail useful to the beginner, in the chapters to follow.

CHAPTER 3

TUNING AND USING WOODEN PLANES

Making a plane behave involves principles common to most of the types to be described. Rather than describing these repeatedly, we will get them out of the way here. If you are proficient in the use of wooden planes, the content of this chapter will be familiar to you, and it may be skipped. If you are not, it will pay to cover them even before you use planes to make your planes.

In most cases, the plane you have made (or even an old one that you are restoring) will not work perfectly the first time you try it. It must be "fettled", to use the old verb, in order to "put it in fine fettle".

Let's review the proper method of using a bench plane such as a jack, smooth or jointer. The workpiece is fixed firmly to the bench top, after examining it for grain direction. It is placed so that the wood fibers slope upward as the plane moves forward. If grain reverses over the surface to be planed, it may be necessary to plane from two different directions. In this case, the final polish planing is made with a very light cut; a circular motion of the smooth plane to effect a slicing cut will help. This may also be required in planing "roey" wood such as some mahogany, where the grain direction changes periodically over the width of the board.

With the plane properly set, only a light grip is needed. Too tight is tiring. (Left-handers will have to change right for left in the following.) The right hand grasps either the rear handle (tote), or the curved rear top of the body for untoted planes; the left hand, palm down, holds the front. For unfenced bench planes, the start of the cut is made with the nose of the plane canted slightly to the left, so that the edge of the work does not meet the cutting edge over its full length at once. At the start, the left hand applies pressure to keep the front of the plane firmly against the work; the right hand pushes forward, not down. (It is good practice for a learner to start the cut using only the left hand, to get the proper feel.) As the cut proceeds,

the thrust is obtained primarily by body movement, not arms alone. Pressure on the front is decreased, and stopped entirely as the end of the work is reached, while downward pressure by the right hand is increased as the stroke ends. The left hand grip may be released, to ensure that the end is not "dubbed" by the plane tipping forward as it leaves the work. The plane is tilted either sidewise or lengthwise (or lifted entirely) as it is returned to start another stroke, to avoid dragging the cutting edge backward in contact with the work.

If the plane stalls as you try to move it forward, don't try to finish the stroke by pushing harder; forcing it will not give a good surface. The iron is not sharp enough for the depth of cut it is set for. Release the iron and reset it. The iron is released by hitting, with a mallet, the forward top of the stock for long bench planes, or the top of the heel for short ones (there are strike buttons in these locations on the better planes). Stubborn wedges may yield to sidewise tapping. The final resort, which has never failed me, is to grip the wedge in a vise with wooden jaws and strike the body of the plane with the heel of the hand, along the direction of the wedge. Make very sure that the iron does not drop free during this operation!

The iron is reset by inserting it in position while the plane rests on the bench top, and lightly seating the wedge. Hold the plane sole upward under a good light, at eye level. Sight along the sole, trying to make it appear almost as a line. (I prefer to sight forward from the heel, but others favor the opposite direction.) If you can see the cutting edge, retract the iron until the edge is no longer seen. Seat the wedge more firmly, and tap gently on the top of the iron with a small mallet until the first glimmer of edge appears. If the glimmer is not uniform over the width of the iron, tap the iron sidewise until it is. Seat the wedge firmly with a mallet tap. Check to make sure that this did not expose more iron; if so, tap the strike button (or the rear of a shorter plane) until the iron retracts and try again. As James Krenov (1977) says, this is like tuning a violin. Initially, it will take a good bit of time to set your plane properly, but with practice it can be done almost as fast as setting a metal plane.

First suspect in poor planing is the keenness of the iron. A new iron is not sharp, but must be honed on an oilstone, waterstone or equivalent to make it so. First of all, the face (the non-beveled side) of the iron must be flat and free of grinding scratches, to the degree that it will take a mirror polish that reflects an undistorted image. For most irons, time is saved by first grinding the face flat on a flat iron plate, using silicon carbide or other abrasive grit, until the entire surface appears uniform. An alternative is to adhere emery paper to a thick piece of plate glass and use this as a lapping plate. The face of the iron is then laid flat on a flat honing stone (diamond by preference, as these do not lose their flatness with use) and rubbed with heavy pressure applied just back of the bevel. Getting the face ready to accept a polish is tiring work, but should be required only once in the life of the blade.

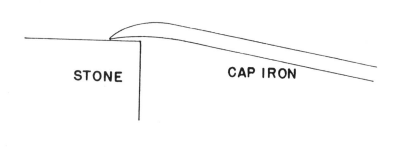

Figure 3:1

There are innumerable methods of sharpening an iron; use the one that suits you or review one of the many books on the subject. For bench plane irons or others with straight edges, I use a honing guide, a mechanical device which holds the iron at a fixed angle to the hone surface, and a diamond stone. Hone until the edge can no longer be seen. (The edge of a dull blade is seen as a thin line of light when viewed edge on under strong light.) Check with a try square

during this process to make sure you are not removing more steel from one side than the other. The diamond stone is followed by either oilstones (soft then hard Arkansas) or two grit sizes of Japanese water stone. The bevel and the lower face of the iron should be polished to a mirror surface for best results. I use the face of a plywood disk charged with automotive stainless steel polishing compound and spun by a slow-speed motor, which changes the cutting angle less than a leather strop does. A hard black Arkansas or a polishing waterstone also serves.

The classical test for edge sharpness is to dry shave the hair on the back of your hand or your arm. I cannot recommend this to you unless you are accustomed to shaving with a straight razor. An alternate test is to take a thin shaving from end grain pine. You will learn the crisp sound a really sharp iron makes as it does this. (Try a new single-edge razor for comparison.) If it doesn't meet either test, the iron needs more work. If it does, treat it with respect!

In many bench plane cases the cap iron will need attention, as well. While it is tightly attached to the cutting iron, try to sight between them. No light should be visible between the bottom of the cap iron and the iron itself. If the contact is not perfect, the cap iron is honed with just the tip in contact with the stone, the body of the cap iron slanted downward off the stone (Fig. 3:1). Only a line contact should be made between the iron and the extreme bottom of the cap, and the contact should be complete over the full width. The contact edge of the cap iron should be sharp - not cutting sharp, but without any surface which will catch the shaving. Polishing the outer edge helps to avoid choking.

"Chatter" is the appearance of periodic ridges across the surface you are planing. It is caused by vibration of the plane iron, and is worse with heavier cuts. It is only to be cured by improving the fit of cap to iron, and reshaping the fit of the wedge in its

14

abutments to ensure that the lower end of the iron is firmly clamped.

"Choking", failure of shavings to leave the throat, may be of several forms. Chatter may cause one form; shavings are caught between the iron and cap iron, and later shavings pile up behind them. If this occurs without chatter, either the two irons are not being held together firmly enough or the fit is poor. In a more common form of choking, a jam appears in the throat above the cutting edge. This happens occasionally even with a good plane taking a heavy cut, and is minimized by keeping an eye on the shavings and clearing them with your fingers at the first sign of hang-up. (The "eyes" were cut in the cheeks of the plane to make this easier.) If it is too frequent, look for an impediment to free shavings flow in the throat of the plane, and correct it. Choking on one side of the mouth may be due to a wedge whose points are too long or improperly tapered.

A third form of choke is accumulation of a tightly packed mass in the mouth in front of the edge, which prevents further cutting. This results either from a poorly shaped cap iron edge (remedied as described above), or (usually only in smooth or polishing planes) from taking a heavier cut than the mouth opening will allow. Either use a finer cut or open the mouth slightly.

Rough cutting is a problem to be expected occasionally even with a fettled plane, when the grain of the work is awkward. If it occurs while planing with the grain in a straight-grained workpiece, suspect the sole of the plane. Check along the length of the sole with a straightedge. If the front of the mouth does not touch it, the sole must be flattened again (wear, or distortion under wedge pressure, can bow the sole). This should be done with the iron inserted with the cutting edge well retracted, and firmly wedged (the pressure of the wedge can force the rear edge of the mouth downward: remember that only the thin cheeks of the plane resist this thrust). The sole is flattened by rubbing on a strip of sanding belt laid on a flat surface such as a jointer bed. In severe cases, it may be necessary to joint the sole by fixing a finely set jointer sole up in a vise and moving your plane over it in a planing motion. Remove no more wood than is necessary. Each resurfacing of the sole will widen the plane's mouth and hurt performance.

A molding plane iron is a bit more difficult to sharpen than one with a straight edge. The face is flattened in the same manner as described for the bench plane irons. The bevel is then honed with an assortment of slips (thin wedge-section oil- or water-stones with rounded edges) having shapes allowing them to reach all sections of the profile. It is important that this honing remove no more from one section of the profile than another. Unless the sharpened blade still matches the sole profile of its plane, it will not cut well. If one section needs more honing than another before it is sharp enough, it will be necessary to continue honing the rest of the already sharp edge to restore the profile.

Having reached keenness over the full edge and satisfied profile matching needs, the bevel may be polished by lightly pressing it against a revolving buffing wheel charged with an emery polishing bar. The face should not be so buffed, as this side should not be rounded even slightly. It may be stropped on leather with the face flat on the strop.

The most common cause (after a dull iron) of poor cutting in a molding plane is lack of agreement between the profiles of the cutting edge and the sole. We will get into this further as we consider making such tools. An old plane, even though it appears in perfect condition and has a sharp iron, may not cut well. Over the years the stock may have shrunk in width enough to impair the iron-to-sole agreement. The only remedy for this is reshaping either sole or iron.

The procedure for using molding planes is quite similar to that outlined above for bench planes, except for the requirement that the plane must follow the same path on each stroke. Other than hollows and rounds, most have an integral fence to ensure this, as well as a depth stop to prevent cutting too deeply. For molding long strips, at least the final stroke should be continuous over its full length, requiring that you walk forward during the stroke. Some workers prefer to start the molding in this case at the far end, moving the starting point of the stroke backwards as the shape develops.

Hollows and rounds, or other molders without fences, require practice to master. To maintain a straight path, it helps to clamp a temporary fence either to the tool or to the workpiece until the cut is well begun. Practice on scrap may help you to outgrow this expedient.

CHAPTER 4

MAKING A SMOOTH PLANE
USING THE LAMINATION METHOD

This is the simplest method for making a bench plane, eliminating the need for a high level of skill in using a chisel. Yet it can produce a plane capable of the finest performance. This type is favored by the master craftsman and teacher James Krenov, who has provided instructions on making and using them (Krenov 1977). One can be made on a kitchen table if your facilities are limited, starting with a kit available from some suppliers of the excellent Hock plane blades. But even starting from scratch, this construction can be accomplished with a minimum of tools.

In the classical one-piece design, both bed and throat front are formed by chisels working in a restricted area. However, the laminated plane is constructed in pieces, allowing complete access to these elements. They are formed by saw cuts and may be planed or scraped, and no skill with a chisel is needed. The construction is seen in Fig. 4:1, which shows the assembly before adding the second side of the plane. The central section is formed of the two core pieces, the rear core contributing the bed and the front core the throat front. In place of the classical wedge abutments, the wedge which tightens the iron is braced against a core pin running across the throat. Another possibility, seen in some very old planes, is to use a metal plate fixed in position across the throat for the wedge to bear against. This can allow more room for shavings clearance, but calls for more care in fitting the wedge.

A table saw is highly desirable for a few critical cuts, but these could be made by very careful use of a good miter box. The most important cut is the one

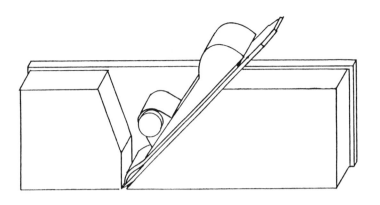

Figure 4:1

which creates the bed, the surface that supports the iron.

IRON Begin by acquiring your iron; it should be on hand while designing the layout. A large hardware store or a tool store will have the modern parallel irons (of constant thickness), or an antique tool dealer may be able to supply the older type which is tapered in thickness. Unless you wish to duplicate the oldest type of bench plane, do not use the antique "uncut" single iron. This has no slot for attachment of a cap iron, and bench planes without these pose problems in use for the inexperienced.

The old planemakers had no need to fit their plane's mouth to a certain blade in their initial layout, as in their day the cutting iron and the cap iron were fairly standard in thickness and shape. Today, you may be using an old iron and cap iron pair, a recent one designed for use in a metal plane, or something in between. Your plane should have its mouth and throat designed to accommodate the blade thickness and particular shape of the cap iron it will use. The plane illustrated uses a 1¾" modern double iron, and the description of its layout illustrates the layout procedure.

WOOD The wood should be chosen with regard to the considerations on species and grain orientation outlined in Chapter 1. Krenov recommends starting with a block wider than the finished size of your plane, and bandsawing it into three pieces, two sides and a core. This provides a uniform appearance, but demands that the four surfaces created be planed perfectly flat before they are glued together. An easier approach is to use the same wood species, not necessarily from the same tree, that may be acquired surface planed to the needed thickness. The thinner sizes of wood are also easier to find. It is safest to use quarter-sawn lumber to make the sides match the stock (both having growth rings parallel to the sole), to equalize the response to humidity changes. This is particularly true with beech, which has more than twice the expansion with moisture content in the direction along the growth rings than across them. It is quite acceptable to use different species of wood for core and sides, as long as they are of comparable hardness and response to humidity variations. Sides of a color contrasting with the core can produce an attractive plane.

MAKING THE CORE The central section or core of the plane starts as a block of hardwood of the length chosen for your plane, thick enough to be planed to a thickness equal to the width of your iron plus 1/16". Unless you have access to a jointer or thickness planer, or are very proficient in the use of a hand plane, it would be wise to have the wood for your core piece machine planed to the proper thickness for you. Since the sides of this plane will be formed by separate pieces which will be glued to the core, the mating surfaces must be truly flat or the glue joints will be weak and unsightly.

The first cut establishes the bed of the plane, and should be made as accurately as possible. The bed should be perfectly flat. If done on a table saw, the blade should be checked for parallelism with the miter gauge slot and its angle should be precisely vertical. It can't hurt to check this, by making a test cut on scrap, to be sure. The location of the cut, the bed line, is marked on the sole (six inches from the heel on the present nine-inch plane). The miter gauge

18

is set to the pitch angle you wish. The usual is 45°, or set the gauge at 40° for a pitch of 50°. The core stock is clamped to the miter gauge (to prevent creep during the miter cut); take care that the clamping does not lift the stock from firm contact with the saw table. The cut is made with care.

The screw which connects the cap iron to the cutting iron prevents the pair from lying flat on the bed. A groove must be made in the surface just cut, to accomodate this screw head. Mark the outline for this recess, centered on the bed and wide enough to clear the screwhead. It runs from the top of the plane down far enough to permit the cutting edge of the iron to protrude slightly beyond the sole. It is cut most conveniently by boring with a Forstner or similar bit at the lower end of the recess, just deep enough to permit the iron to seat against the bed. The recess is extended upward by chisel and a hand router such as the Stanley #271. A razor saw to cut the sides of the recess is helpful. The rear section of core after this operation is seen in Fig. 4:2.

With the irons bedded in cutting position, note the profile of the cap iron. Plan the shape of the sole end of the front of the throat to provide for easy shavings escape, when the plane is used. Most bench planes slope this surface toward the heel of the plane, to minimize mouth widening as the plane wears or the sole is resurfaced. Cap irons intended for metal planes often bulge upward near their lower end, and do not leave enough room for shaving to pass through a lower throat with the conventional backward slope. With the irons used in the present case, the front of the throat has to rise vertically from the mouth. If your iron pair permits, this lower throat front should slope backward, toward the heel, at an angle of about 70° from the horizontal.

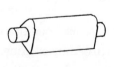

After the initial rise for a half-inch or so, the front of the throat should slant forward to allow room for fingers to clear away shavings in the event of a choke. (Seventy degrees

Figure 4:3

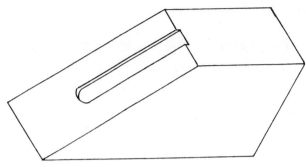

Figure 4:2

from horizontal was used here). Scribe the two lines defining this profile on the remaining piece of core stock, and cut it to form the throat front. (Saving wood by turning this remaining piece upside down is not a good idea; you want identical grain surfaces on both ends of the sole.) The bed and throat front profiles are scraped and/or sanded smooth at this point; it's much more difficult later. The shape of the front core piece may be seen in Fig. 4:1.

CORE PIN   In place of the usual wedge abutments, this type of construction most often uses a core pin to hold the wedge against the iron. Although a simple dowel could be used, this will dent under pressure and allow the wedge to drift downward with time. It is better to provide a flat surface for the wedge to bear against. The pattern used by Krenov (1977) shown in the drawing (Fig. 4:3) is a good one. Tenons are cut on square stock, and the central profile is whittled or planed out. (The tenons, too, may be whittled, but a better fit is obtained by using a lathe. Another option is gluing a dowel inside a hole drilled through the central piece.) The core pin will be held in position by fitting the tenons into holes in the sides of the stock. The length of the central portion of the core pin, the part with the flat surface, is made just under the core width. The tenons take the full thrust of the wedge, and should not be undersize; the tool illustrated used a diameter of $\frac{5}{8}$", but $\frac{1}{2}$" should be adequate. The diameter must closely match that of the hole made by the drill you plan to use for their seats, just loose enough to turn easily.

PLANE SIDES The two sides of the plane are now cut out, a bit oversize to allow for adjustment in assembly, and planed to a thickness of $\frac{3}{8}$". (The glue sides of these must be flat and true.) Lay the front and rear sections of the core on one of the sides, and determine the location for the core pin. This should place the flat side of the pin about 3/8" from the bed of the core, and the hole for the cylindrical pivot tenon should be as low as is consistent with a clear path for shavings to escape. (It was centered $1\frac{3}{4}$" above the sole for the tool illustrated.) Mark the chosen location for the hole center, place the outer faces of the two sides together (to avoid visible splintering), and drill through both for the core pin tenons. A drill press or great care is needed to make sure these are square to the sides.

This completes the pieces required for the stock. As in any woodworking project, it is a good idea to assemble the parts without glue to make sure that you will have no surprises, and to have the needed clamps on hand and set to approximate size openings. Note the clearance between core pin and bed to guide your shaping of the wedge.

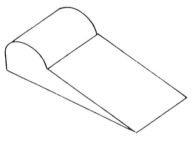

Figure 4:4

ASSEMBLY This is less hectic if done in stages. Proper location of the two core pieces is critical to the plane's performance. A safe procedure is to clamp the two pieces of the core, sole down, to a flat surface (with waxed paper under them). They are positioned as they will be in the final tool. With the blade on the bed, its cutting edge resting on the wax paper, the cutting edge should touch the front core section. (Plan for zero shavings clearance or slightly less at this point; the mouth can be opened

out later). Spread glue on one side of both core pieces and clamp the side securely to the core. (Yellow Carpenter's glue was used here, but the new moisture cure urethane glue might be even better.) Make sure that the clamping does not disturb the contact of the sole of both core pieces with the flat wax paper surface; if the soles of the two core pieces do not lie in the same plane after glue-up, they will have to be made so by planing, with a bad effect on the mouth opening.

While the glue is drying, you will have time to make the wedge. The shape used (Fig. 4:4) is, again, copied from Krenov, but the upper portion may be shaped to any design you wish as long as its top will not be damaged by the mallet blows used to seat it. The lower section tapers to a very thin point, at an angle (about 10°) which puts this bottom edge as far down as possible on the cap iron.

The other side of the stock may now be glued on. The core pin is inserted into its hole in the side already assembled, and wedge and iron are placed in position as shown in Fig. 4:1. Glue is spread on the open sides of the core. The second side is placed in position, with the core pin tenon seated in it. Adjust the placement of the second side to ensure that the wedge seats firmly against the flat surface of the core pin and the iron over its full width, and that the core pin axis is parallel to the sole. Clamp securely until dry.

FINISHING STEPS The sole is now planed to equalize the level of core and sides, and excess material from the sides is trimmed off. The planarity of the sole is checked by seating the blade firmly with its cutting edge well retracted, and running the assembled plane in a planing motion over a strip of sanding belt or pieces of sandpaper placed on a flat surface (jointer bed or iron tablesaw table). All areas of the sole should sand evenly. (The iron should be wedged tightly during this step, as the sole will be minutely distorted by the pressure of the wedge and you wish to make the sole flat under the conditions of use.) The iron is then advanced to cutting position. If there is insufficient room in front of the cutting edge for a thin shaving to pass, the mouth is CARE-

FULLY opened with a thin file. The most common problem in performance of first planes is letting the mouth opening become too wide. In the present case, the sanding of the sole had provided the correct mouth opening for a finishing smooth, or "polishing" plane. The mouth opening was $\frac{1}{8}$"; with the plane blade used, the front of the mouth was less than $\frac{1}{32}$" in front of the cutting edge.

A test cut will show up any problems at this point. The tool illustrated behaved beautifully from the first, leaving a polished surface and removing a shaving which was measured by micrometer at four thousandths of an inch thick. If your new plane does not perform satisfactorily, refer to the "fettling" procedures detailed earlier in Chapter 3.

The stock is now shaped to suit your pleasure. At a minimum, the top rear should be rounded for a comfortable grip, and top edges chamfered or rounded. In the plane illustrated, the sides at the top of the throat had "eyes" cut, but this was the last concession to the classical shape. After sanding, this shape was a bit slippery to hold. A thumb depression was cut with a gouge, and diagonal grooves cut in the right side for finger traction. (I have long felt that the dents claimed to have been worn into tools by horny hands after long use, were probably carved there by their owners for comfort.)

Sanding and two coats of boiled linseed oil (the first thinned 1:1 with turpentine), rubbed in and wiped off, finished my tool. This is my usual choice, but some coating alternates are given in Chapter 6.

CHAPTER 5

TWO-PIECE CONSTRUCTION : JACK PLANE

This method of making bench plane stocks is intermediate in difficulty between the lamination method just described, and the classical method to be described in the next chapter. Dividing the plane stock into two halves longitudinally permits the bed, abutments, and throat front to be sawn, rather than chiseled. This can produce accurate surfaces even for inexperienced chisel users. It does require the use of chisels to shape the sides of the throat, but these are much less critical to plane performance. Another advantage of this construction method (and of the lamination method) is that today it is much easier to find hardwood of thicknesses suitable to these techniques than it is to locate the three-inch (twelve-quarter) material needed for the classical method.

The previous method of construction places the full thrust of the wedge on the glue joints, and creates the danger of glue joint creep, over time, with result-ing mouth widening. (I have seen no evidence of this in my planes, but they haven't been in use long enough to guarantee that they won't creep over a few decades.) The present method does not have this drawback, the thrust being carried by the wood in the same manner as in a classical type. You will some-times see tools that were made in this way by English users (not professional planemakers) in the early twentieth century.

THE CLASSICAL THROAT This construc-tion project provides a good introduction to the clas-sical shape of the throat front, which is difficult to present clearly in the two dimensions of a paper surface. I cannot emphasize strongly enough that the wisest path to planemaking is to acquire an antique wooden plane of the type you want to make, and use it as a prototype. Features of the throat which become quite clear, when seen in the actual plane, may require study of drawings and careful reading of some difficult text before these can be translated into a three-dimensional mental image. Once this is attained, however, the task to be accomplished becomes quite clear.

If a real plane is not available, the throat will be shown in a variety of drawings here and in later chapters. Become familiar with them, and have a clear idea of the shape you are attempting to create. The first of these (Fig. 5:1) is intended as a view looking down into the completed throat of the right half of this plane, at an angle which makes the bed of the plane appear as a straight line.

The lower front of the throat, which rises from the mouth slanting back toward the heel, is called the wear. (The wear of the present plane, for reasons which we will get into later, is much shorter than usual.) The throat front breaks to a forward slope for its upper section, and is as wide as the bed at the top of the stock. In front of the bed, the side of the plane juts inward to form the abutment, against which the wedge will press. The side of the throat meets the top of the stock in a diagonal line, running from the throat front to the tip of the abutment.

The front of the throat cannot be kept at the full width of the mouth as it moves toward the wear, as this would weaken the abutments. It shrinks inwards as it drops downward, roughly paralleling the diagonal line on top of the stock. Because of this narrowing of the upper throat front, the line where it meets the wear is not as wide as the mouth. The side of the

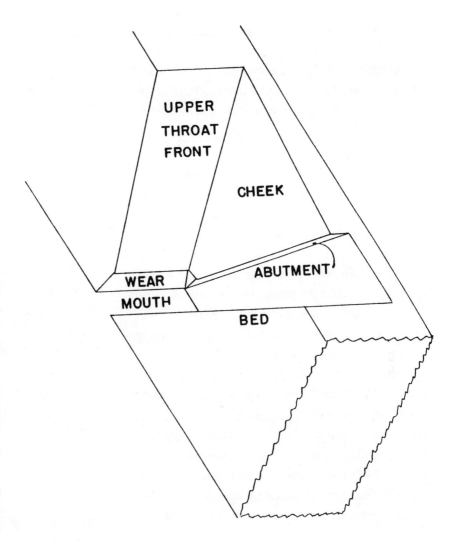

Figure 5:1

throat, called the cheek, is bounded at its front by this sloping side of the throat front; at its top, by the diagonal joining the side of the throat to the tip of the abutment; and at its rear by the inner edge of the abutment (which maintains its one-quarter inch wedge grip surface as far down as possible).

The wear (lower throat front) must be widened below its meeting with the upper throat front, to reach the full width of the mouth. The small triangle seen at the side of the wear in the sketch shows where wood was removed to accomplish this, and also to slope away the lower ends of the abutment. Both are required to allow a clear path for the shavings as they move upward.

23

PROTOTYPE The plane illustrated was patterned after one made (by the classical method) by the Auburn Tool Co. sometime between 1864 and 1893, probably by inmates of Auburn prison. Modifications were made to accomodate this method of construction and a modern 2⅜" double iron.

INITIAL LAYOUT The two halves of the hardwood stock (I used maple) are cut and squared to the size 16 x 2¾ x 1⁹⁄₁₆". The sides to be glued together in final assembly should be perfectly flat. As I was unable at the time to locate hardwood of the optimum grain orientation, I settled for 45° annual rings, and matched the two halves for a symmetrical ring pattern on toe and heel; fortunately, the grain was straight enough that this did not violate the warning against rising grain toe to heel.

The mouth line is marked across both sole halves at five inches from the toe, and the bed line is scribed parallel to this and ⅜" nearer the heel. The side projection of the bed line is marked on all four vertical surfaces, from the sole bedline and rising at a slant of 45° toward the heel, as shown in Fig.5:2. The side bedlines are joined by squaring a line between them on top of the two halves of the stock.

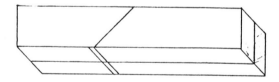

Figure 5:2

The lower throat front (wear) of the prototype slopes toward the heel at an angle of 75° for a bit more than an inch, then breaks to a forward slope of 65° for the upper throat front, as shown in Fig. 5:3. This shows (by the dotted line) that it would not be possible to cut the throat front to this profile with a circular saw blade without cutting away a portion of the sole behind the bedline. It is necessary to modify the throat front profile to accommodate the construction method. An upper throat front angle of 70°, placed to just clear the bedline on the sole, gives a proper throat

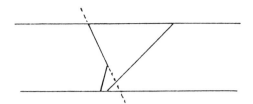

Figure 5:3

opening on top of the stock. Allowing for the thin kerf of the sawblade, this leaves room for a wear only ⅜" high at the 75° slope of the prototype. The required modification will not change plane performance unless the sole is worn and resurfaced for more than ⅜". This throat front profile is marked on all four vertical surfaces, as shown in Fig.5:4. The profile of the blade and cap iron used is also sketched in. Be sure that your cap iron does not narrow the passage through which the shavings must pass; if it does, the wear must be cut at a higher angle.

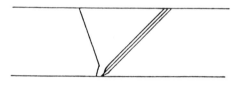

Figure 5:4

The mouth of the plane should be made ¹⁄₁₆" wider than the width of your iron, 2⁷⁄₁₆" in the present case. (The clearance permits adjustment to correct for a cutting edge less than perfectly square to the iron side.) Half of this distance is marked off from the inner side of each half of the sole, and lines are scribed on the sole between the bed and mouth lines to locate the extremities of the mouth. The same measurement is made on the tops of each half, and lines are scribed forward from the top bedline to mark the sides of the wedge slots.

CUTTING THE BED The bed is formed by matching saw cuts on each half. This is a most critical step in determining plane performance, and requires great care. The bench saw blade is made precisely vertical, checked by a trial cut on scrap. The miter gauge is set at the 45° angle, using a good protractor (the setting is changed to the opposite direction of slope for the cut in the other half, and the cuts must match). The workpiece is clamped to the miter gauge, with location set to cut exactly on the side bed lines, the kerf being toward the toe. (Clamping guards against creep; make sure that your clamping does not lift the workpiece from contact with the saw table.)

The height of the blade is set to cut just to the mark indicating the side of the bed, a height of $1^7/_{32}$" in the present case (a height gauge is helpful, as repeating the cut to adjust the height risks marring the bed surface). Recheck everything, and cut carefully. The miter gauge is reset to 45° in the other direction, and the process is repeated with the other half of the stock.

CUTTING THE ABUTMENTS   The next cut defines the abutments which will hold the wedge in place. Measure forward from the bedline on top of the stock a distance of $1^1/_8$". With the two halves held together, their bedline cuts mating, scribe a line across both tops, marking the abutment location. Scribe lines on the inner sides of both halves joining the ends of this line with the mouth line on their soles.

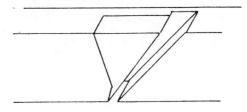

Figure 5:5

The miter gauge angle is reset at 36° to cut the 54° angle of the abutment line, and the stock side clamped in position to cut exactly on the line with the kerf toward the heel. With bed and abutment cuts made, the waste between the cuts may be nibbled away by more cuts, taking care not to mar the mouth. Repeat the entire sequence with the other half of the stock. The nibbled region between the abutment cut and the bed is now cleaned with paring chisels, to the level of the outer edge of the wedge slots. The result is shown in Fig.5:5.

CUTTING THE THROAT FRONT   The line defining the upper throat front is scribed on the inner

sides of the two halves, sloping forward at 70° from the bedline on the soles.

Decrease the tablesaw blade height by $1/_4$" (it should be a thin kerf blade). Set the mortise gauge at 20° to cut the 70° upper slope of the throat front. Clamp the piece in position to have the saw kerf just clear the sole bedline, and make the cut. Reset the miter gauge to the same angle on the other side, and repeat with the other half of the stock.

The lower throat front is formed by changing the miter gauge angle to that required to cut along the line determined above (Fig. 5:4) by the clearance requirements of your plane iron (75° rearward slope in the present case, calling for a miter setting of 15°). Clamp the side of the stock to the miter gauge in position to place the kerf behind the mouth line on the sole, and make the cut. Again repeat with the other half. The waste between the abutment cut and the throat front may be removed with chisels, keeping well short of the tip of the abutment.

FINISHING THE THROAT   The front of the throat needs to be widened to roughly the same extent as the wedge notches. The saw cut defining the upper throat is deepened with a slanting cut of a back saw. This continues the plane of the earlier sawcut, reaching a point $1/_4$" from the outer side of the stock at the top of the piece, but does not deepen the cut at the break in the throat front.

A slanting line is drawn on the top, from the inner end of the abutment to the point where this deepened cut emerges. The throat sides are now pared away with chisels, on a slanting surface bounded by this diagonal line, the bottom of the backsaw cut and the inner edge of the abutment. The shaded surfaces in Fig. 5:6 show the volume removed.

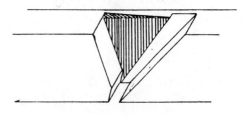

Figure 5:6

25

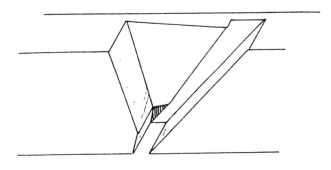

Figure 5:7

Do not be concerned by the fact that the cheek is not perfectly flat. Since it is bounded by two lines which are not in the same plane, it cannot be. The deviation is too small to be noticeable until you are cutting it. Close examination of your prototype will reveal a slight warp or curve in its cheek surface.

The lower end of the cheek must be removed to allow clear passage for shavings at the ends of the mouth opening. This is done by paring away the wedge-shaped volume at the bottom of the abutments, from the outer edge of the mouth opening to the bottom of the cut described in the preceding paragraph. The shaded area shown in Fig.5:7 shows the volume removed.

Two final steps may be done now, or can wait until the halves are glued together. The "eyes" of the plane, which make it easier for fingers to remove shavings from the throat, are cut with a sharp paring chisel to the outline shown in Fig.2:1. The slot in the bed to provide clearance for the head of the screw holding cap iron and cutting iron together is made just deep enough to allow the plane iron to seat on the bed.

ALTERNATE LAY-OUT PROCEDURE
To recapitulate the lines marked in the above sequence, the drawings of Fig.5:8 show all of the lay-out lines, should you wish to complete them before starting to cut. These are isometric views of the throat area, those on the left as seen from above and those on the right from below. The lettered locations are primed for the left-hand half-stock (remember that the left side of the plane is on your left as you use it, with the heel facing you).

Scribe the mouth lines (AB and A'B') across the soles of the two halves, five inches from the toe; and another pair, the bed lines CD and C'D', ⅜" behind it. From the sole bed line, scribe lines DE and D'E',

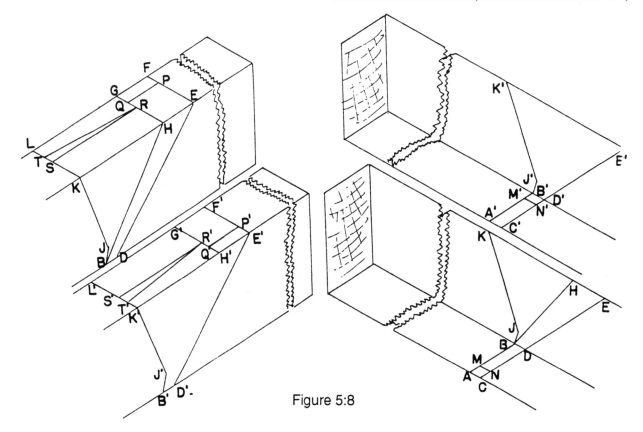

Figure 5:8

CF and C'F' on both sides of each half, slanting upward toward the heel at the pitch angle of 45°. Join these lines by scribing EF and E'F' across the top of each half, and recheck if not square. The abutment lines GH and G'H' are scribed across the tops 1⅛" forward of this.

The lines BJ and B'J' marking the wear (lower throat front) are scribed on both sides of the two halves rising at 75° of backward slant (or other angle as determined by the requirements of your cap iron) from the sole mouth line for a short distance. The upper throat front lines JK and J'K' rise at a forward slant of 70° from the bed lines CD, C'D' on the sole, and the front of the throat is marked by the lines KL, K'L' across the top of the stock.

The ends of the mouth, MN and M'N' are marked to make the mouth width ⅟₁₆" wider than the width of the plane iron. PQ and P'Q' mark the same width at the top of the stock to place the sides of the wedge slots. Measure ¼" inward to mark the tip of the abutments, and scribe RS,R'S'to the front of the throat. The diagonals RT and R'T' run from the tips of the abutments to ¼" from the outer sides, to mark the widening of the throat forward of the abutments.

TOTE MORTISE   The mortise for the handle of the plane may now be marked out, with the two sides of the plane clamped together. This is four inches long, the aft end being a 1" semicircle, and the front end square, 2" behind the bed line. Its depth is ⅝". It may be cut now by clamping the two sides of the stock together and drilling a 1" hole with a Forstner bit at the aft end, then completing the mortise with chisels with the two halves separated. It is preferable to wait until after glue-up and cut the mortise with a Forstner bit, chisels and hand router (even better, with an end mill in a drill press cross vise).

ASSEMBLY   In preparation for glue-up, the two halves of the plane body are placed on a flat surface, such as your table saw bed, on waxed paper. The glue is spread, and the two halves carefully aligned to make the bed cuts of the two halves agree perfectly. Make sure that this alignment does not shift while clamping the halves together.

TOTE   While the glue is drying, the tote may be made; an outline is shown in Fig. 5:9. This is cut from hardwood a full 1" thick with a bandsaw or turning saw. The handgrip edges are rounded to semicircles with drawknife, spokeshave and rasps, and sanded smooth. Defer profiling the lower portion until you can test-fit it into the stock mortise. Then the lower heel end of the tote is carefully shaped to match the semicircle end of the mortise in the stock. Only after this has been done to your satisfaction is the forward end of the tote trimmed to fit (use a slight slope to wedge it home), and the bottom of the tote trimmed to make its forward end flush with the top of the stock.

WEDGE   The wedge is made from 5/8" or thicker wood, cut to the width of the abutment area of the throat (2 7/16"). Its taper is approximately determined by tracing the outline of the side of the assembled cap iron and iron above the bed line (DE of Fig.5:8) marked on the stock (with the edge of the iron placed in cutting position). The wedge will fill the space between this tracing and the abutment line BH. Measure the taper, and saw the wedge to match (a bandsaw with table carefully set square to the blade is convenient). A set of wedge gauges (thin wooden strips cut to different tapers), simplifies this step and is worth making if you plan to make more than one plane.

Before test fitting this, it may be necessary to cut a recess in the back of the wedge to accommodate the protrusion of the cap screw above the cap iron surface. This is easily accomplished with a Forstner bit. Do not make it any

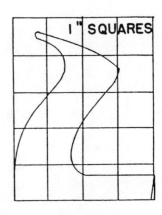

Figure 5:9

27

deeper than necessary.

With the wedge snugly against the top of the cap iron (some trimming may be required to accommodate a bulge at the bottom of your cap iron), the two are inserted to the wedge mortise. Note the fit to the ears of the abutments. This must be painstakingly adjusted, with paring chisels and floats, until the wedge contacts both abutments over its full length. Do not rush this step: it is important to performance. Done properly, a light tap on top of the wedge with a mallet will seat it so firmly that it is not easily withdrawn. Because it often happens that repeated adjustment of wedge angle shortens the wedge, it is a good idea to allow extra length in the wedge blank.

Fitting completed and wedge and iron in place, mark lines on the top surface of the wedge where the abutments grip it. The wood between these lines at the bottom of the wedge must be removed to permit shavings to escape freely. My prototype has a rather unusual wedge (shown in Fig. 5:10) in that less of its lower end was removed than normal; you may prefer to use the more conventional style which continues the sloped cut-out up to the level of the top of the stock (see Fig. 6:5). To duplicate the one shown in 5:10, the wood between the lines is sawn away to a line across the wedge ¾" above its bottom. Another line is drawn ¾" above this, and the area between the two horizontal lines tapered to a rather sharp point,

with a paring chisel. The upper portion of the wedge is shaped to your preference; that shown in the sketch is often seen.

Because the iron is released from the plane by striking the top front of the stock with a mallet, it is a good idea to install a strike button there to avoid unsightly marring. This is a short (⅝") cylinder of hardwood, fitted end grain up into a hole drilled in the top of the stock half-way between toe and throat front. This and the tote are glued in place after final polish planing of the stock.

The final steps are slight rounding of the top rear edge, rounding the side top edges, and chamfering the vertical edges with a paring chisel, terminating these with gouge cuts. Your plane is now ready for fettling (see Chapter 3). With smooth cutting at-

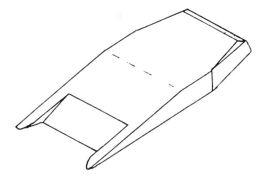

Figure 5:10

tained, finish with the coating of your choice. The plane shown received two coats of boiled linseed oil well rubbed in (the first thinned 1:1 with turpentine).

CHAPTER 6

BENCH PLANES BY THE CLASSICAL METHOD
(COACHMAKER'S SMOOTH PLANE)

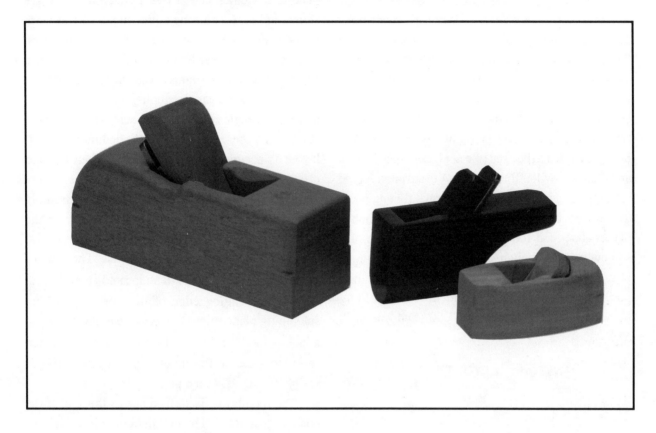

The bench planes are presumably so-called because they were used so often that they were more apt to be found on the workbench than on a shelf. The most common types are the smooth (6.5-9" long, unless it has a handle), the jack (usually 14"-16"), fore (18"-22") and jointer (22"-30"). The names of the parts of the jack plane shown in Fig. 2:1 apply to all of the others. You may appreciate the tradesman's preference for choosing the names of parts of the body for the plane parts that suggested them. The mouth, the slot on the bottom of the plane that "eats" the shavings, passes them through the throat.

The throat design has been honed by generations of makers, and is basically the same for all of the bench planes. Forming this critical part of plane architecture uses essentially the same procedure for all of these tools. In fact, almost any plane which

allows the shavings to escape from an opening in the top of the stock has a very similar throat, and it is cut in the same manner. The following description will serve for any of them, with minor variations which will be covered in individual cases later.

It is far easier to make a plane if you have a good prototype to follow. If you do not, be sure that you have a clear picture of the throat architecture. The sketches in the previous chapter may be helpful in clarifying those used here.

Acquire your wood, choose a proper orientation and square the stock with regard to the requirements spelled out in Chapter 1. Unless you are better with a handsaw than I am, use either a carefully aligned table saw or a good miter box. Before beginning layout of a smooth plane or any one which requires a small mouth opening, your cutting iron and cap iron should be on hand. An old pair designed for a wooden plane, with the cutter tapered in thickness, may often be obtained from an antique tool dealer. A pair made for a current metal plane will serve, and these are available from many large tool stores.

THROAT LAYOUT   The throat is normally centrally located in the width of the stock and near the midpoint of the length of the plane, or a bit further forward for planes fitted with rear handles. If the plane is to have a tote (handle), enough distance between throat and handle is allowed to permit insertion and removal of the cutting iron without interference. The pitch to be used (the angle between the iron and the sole), will influence this. A usual pitch for the longer planes is 45°, and this is normal for any plane to be used on soft woods. Cabinetmaker's bench planes, intended for hardwood use, are often at a somewhat higher pitch. The old names reflect this. "Common" pitch is 45°, "Cabinet" pitch, or half pitch, is 60° (normally found only in molding planes). Intermediate are "York", 50°, and "middle", 55°.

INITIAL   LAYOUT

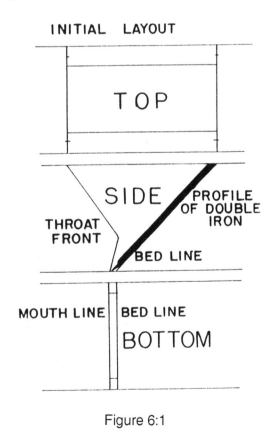

Figure 6:1

Choose the pitch and throat location (or better, measure these from a plane you have chosen as your prototype). The location of the bed surface, the rear boundary of the throat on which the cutting iron will rest, is to be located by lines scribed on the stock. (These and other lines to be described below are shown in Fig. 6:1) Scribe a line on the sole to mark the point at which the bed surface intersects it, which will become the rear boundary of the sole opening (the mouth). From the ends of this line, mark bedlines on the sides of the stock, sloping up and to the rear, at the pitch angle chosen. A line across the top of the stock joins the ends of the side bedlines. If your layout is accurate and the stock has been squared properly, this line will be square to the sides.

The side profile of the iron and cap iron assembly (with the cap iron set as close as possible to the cutting edge) is marked on one of the side bed lines, in the position the iron will take in use. The front of the mouth of the plane is to be located about $\frac{1}{16}$" in front of the cutting edge of the iron (a polishing smoothing plane might use zero clearance to begin, a jack plane $\frac{1}{8}$"). Err on the small side; it is much easier to increase the mouth opening than it is to shrink it, in the finished plane.

The mouth line is scribed across the sole at the position just noted. The mouth outline is completed by scribing its sides equally spaced from the sides of the stock, leaving a mouth extending from side to side a distance $\frac{1}{16}$" wider than the width of the iron. This clearance permits leeway in placing the iron to compensate for a cutting edge less than perfectly square to the sides of the iron. It also is a margin of safety to allow for width shrinkage of the stock as the wood ages. (Old planes often have irons tightly gripped by the sides because of this shrinkage.)

The throat front of the classic plane is designed as a compromise between two objectives. One, it must allow the shavings to escape without impediment, and let the fingers reach any that are caught in the throat. This calls for lots of room in front of the cutter edge. Two, the sole will wear with time, and will periodically require dressing to restore flatness. This removes wood, and if the front of the throat

30

slopes forward, the throat will widen and the cut will suffer. No widening would be experienced if the lower throat front sloped back at the bed angle, but this would risk shavings hangup. The compromise is a backward slope somewhat steeper than the bed angle, for the lower throat front.

In a typical profile, the front of the throat begins at the mouth line on the sole and slants backward at 75° for an inch or so (this surface being called the "wear"), then breaks to a forward slope from there to the top of the stock. The allowable slope of the lower section is limited by the profile of your cap iron, already sketched on the side of the stock. This slope must permit at least the same clearance between the hump of the cap iron and the wear, or lower front of the throat, as is allowed between the cutting edge and the front of the mouth. Do not widen the mouth to allow this, but if need be, make the slope of the wear steeper.

Lines marking the outline of the throat front are marked on both sides, the wear line sloping back at the angle just chosen and the top front sloping forward at an angle to give a reasonable top opening (55-70°, or the angle measured on your prototype). These lines on the side are joined by a line across the top of the stock, at right angles to the sides, marking the top front of the throat opening. Both this line and the bedline mark on top of the stock are marked for width, again $1/16$" wider than the width of the iron and centrally placed.

The "ears" of the plane, the projections which grip the wedge, extend inward from the sides of the throat, forming the abutments. An abutment face of $1/4$" is common, larger for very big planes, less for

smaller. Rather than trying to shape abutments while sinking the throat, it is easier to make the initial excavation with straight sides just touching the tips of the ears. Scribe lines on the top of the stock between bed and throat front, equally spaced from the sides and separated by the width of your iron less $7/16$". The layout lines at this point are shown in Fig. 6:1.

CUTTING THE THROAT   All of the wood within these lines and within the bed and front lines marked on the sides of the stock must now be removed. Be prepared to spend many hours in this operation in your first attempt, as rushing it will not produce satisfactory results. It helps to start the process by boring holes well within these outlines. It is very easy to exceed the limits, so proceed with caution. Continue with a mortise chisel and mallet, taking pains to stay well within the bounds marked. As fairly heavy blows will be required, it helps to rest the sole on a piece of soft wood rather than on the hard wood of your bench, to prevent sole marring from wood chips that find their way under it. Do not break through the sole. When the excavation has reached to a depth within about $1/2$" from the sole, turn the stock over and outline the mouth with a sharp chisel. Sink a depression for a fraction of an inch within the mouth outline (remembering not to trespass on the backward slope of the mouth front). Drill through from the center of this depression, at an angle slightly steeper than the bed angle, until you break through into the earlier cut. This helps to keep track of the progress of your cut from the top of the stock, and warns you when to stop to avoid having the mortise chisel break through and damage the mouth. You may choose to drill several more holes and rough out the lower section of the throat with a fine keyhole saw or coping saw.

Having come as close as is prudent with mallet and mortise chisel, cutting the throat is continued with paring chisels. The bed must be carefully pared to form a perfectly flat surface. This supports the iron, and if any irregularity allows rocking to occur as the plane is used, its performance will suffer. Experi-

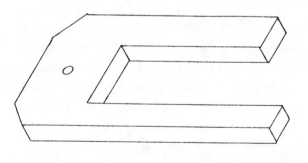

Figure 6:2

enced planemakers could pare freehand, leaning on a broad "bedding" chisel with their shoulder. (They used a simple "sinking-down" or bedding guide, shown in Fig. 6:2, to check their progress. This is easily made, and is quite helpful. One leg is placed within the throat excavation and the other leg is compared with the side bedline. Unless you make planes for a living or have delicate control of great strength, make do with narrower chisels, an inch or less wide. Plan your cuts so that each stroke can be continued for the full length of the bed. If you are forced to stop short of this because of too much resistance, you are attempting to cut too deeply. It is frighteningly easy to slip below the desired bed level, leaving a scar in the bed that must be lived with. It is worth while (at least for your first attempt) to clamp a block, cut to the bed angle, to the top of the stock and to keep a long paring chisel flat against it during this operation. Move the block backward periodically, keeping the parings thin enough for easy control. If you have used paring chisels before, you

and a poorly cut surface damages the appearance of your plane.

The bed must now be widened by cutting away the slots that grip the wedge and iron. You have already located the position of the front of the cap iron with a line on the side of your plane, when you determined the mouth position. The back of the wedge presses on the flat section of the cap iron, so the straight section of your line defines the position of the rear of the wedge. It is now necessary to locate the position of the front of the wedge, which determines the position of the abutments.

The classical tapered iron had a cap iron with a simple bend at its bottom. An iron intended for a metal plane often has a double curve, rising up then curving down to the iron. In either case, the abutment line (the line marking the position of the front of the wedge) is drawn at an angle eight to ten degrees more than the pitch angle and a sixteenth inch or so above the level at which it would run into the high point of the cap iron. An abutment line is drawn on each side

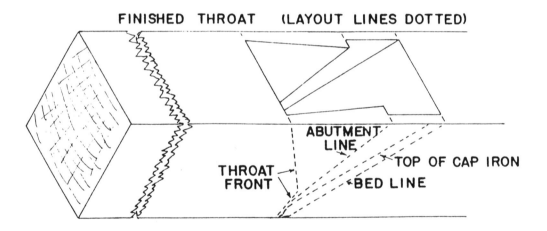

Figure 6:3

know that time spent in honing them saves time and temper in the long run. Unless they are truly sharp, satisfactory results will elude you.

With this section of the bed finished to your satisfaction, the throat front is pared in a similar manner, guided by the profile lines on the sides of the stock. While not as crucial to plane performance as the bed surface, the throat front is much more visible

of the stock. Join these with a line (which should be at right angles to the sides) across the remaining top of the stock. This will be used to guide the cutting of the abutments. The rear of the wedge slots is the bed surface. These layout lines are seen in Fig. 6:3.

The next step is to extend the bed surface outward on both sides to reach its full width (the iron width plus $\frac{1}{16}$"). Professional planemakers used a special saw for this step, a thick blade shaped like a small compass saw and without set. A fine saw will serve (a Japanese detail saw, like a keyhole saw, is useful here). Do not mar the bed surface; keep far enough away from the line to leave a margin of safety to be pared away.

The abutments are then sawn, guided by the abutment lines on the sides and top of the stock. The isometric sketch of Fig. 6:4 gives a view of the throat that would be obtained by breaking the stock away through the mouth opening. It shows that, in many cases, the abutment surfaces would pierce the mouth front if cut through. They are sawn from the top of the stock as far as possible and finished with chisels.

The waste between the two saw cuts (bed and abutment) may now be cleared with chisels (a pair of skew chisels, ground with slanted cutting edges, is useful here). The sawn extension of the bed is pared, making sure that it continues the flat bed surface pared earlier. The professional planemaker used floats to finish the wedge slot surfaces and fit the wedge. Although floats may call to mind very coarse files, they have in fact a series of scraping edges which can remove wood rapidly yet leave a smooth finish. They are easily made, and well worth making if you plan to make more than one plane; details are given on p.61. The same result may be obtained, much more slowly, with small files.

The front of the throat is now widened on top of the stock for easier chip clearance, as shown in Fig. 6:3. Diagonal lines are drawn from the tips of the wedge abutments forward to the points on the line marking the throat front at the full width of the mouth. The throat front is extended outward with a saw cut until it meets this line. The saw cut should not be of uniform depth; it should not cut into the side at the point where the upper throat front and the wear meet. Each cheek is then pared away to the depth of this saw cut, creating a surface defined and bounded by the bottom of the saw cut, the diagonal on top of the stock, and the inner edge of the abutment.

This leaves the throat still not the full width of the mouth of the plane at the sole. Below the break between the slopes of the throat front (the point at

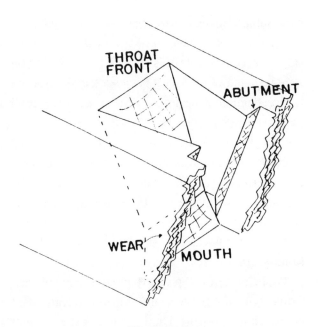

Figure 6:4

which the last cut terminated), chisel cuts are used to widen the side walls of the throat, sloping them outward to meet the sides of the mouth. This removes a portion of the lower end of the abutment surfaces. The throat at this point is sketched in Figs. 6:3 and 4.

The "eyes" are present to ease entry of the fingers when shavings must be cleared from the throat. They are cut with a sharp chisel to resemble those shown in Fig. 2:1.

One more step completes the throat, finishing the most difficult part of plane making. A slot must be cut in your carefully pared bed, to accommodate the head of the screw which holds cap iron and cutting iron together. This should be centered, slightly wider than the screw head, running from the top of the stock low enough to permit the plane iron to protrude well below the stock. It may be started with a Forstner bit for the low end and finished with chisels or a router. The Jack plane sketch (Fig. 2:1) shows this.

MAKING THE WEDGE   A blank is squared to the width of the throat, thicker than required to fill the top of the wedge slots behind the abutments, and a few inches longer than you wish the final wedge to be. The lower end is tapered to match the angle drawn on the sides of the stock between the abutment line and the level top of the cap iron. If your double iron has a humped lower end to its cap iron, the lower edge of the wedge will have to be trimmed on its under side to accommodate this. It will be easier if you remove some of the wood between the sides of the wedge, beginning the process described in the second paragraph below.

Insert wedge and iron, and note where wood must be removed from the wedge to permit contact over the full length of the abutments. Proceed slowly, one stroke of a plane at a time, until the match is attained. It may be necessary to pare the abutment surfaces if the two wedge slots are not of exactly the same shape (a set of wedge gauges, described on p.108, helps here). A properly fitted wedge will seat firmly with a light tap, and will not release with simple finger pressure. Until you have experience in this phase, it will take a considerable amount of time. Matching the fit on both sides of the wedge may recall the situation of sawing off the ends of a chair leg to stop a wobble. Extra length has been allowed in the length of the wedge blank to allow for the losses of trial and error.

With proper fit attained, the lower edge of the wedge is cut off at the point where the cap iron slopes away from it. The lower central area of the wedge must be removed to allow for shavings clearance. With wedge and iron in place, run a pencil down the upper face of the wedge along the abutments on both sides. A line is drawn across the wedge, between these lines and at the level of the top of the plane body. A second line is drawn half-way between this line and the bottom of the wedge. The area between the abutment outlines and this second line is sawn away with coping or bandsaw. The area above this cut-out is tapered down to a feather edge, between the upper line and this cut, as shown in Fig. 6:5. The lower end of the two points at the bottom of the wedge are tapered away to match the abutment profile. Do not leave the pointed tips of the wedge too sharp and fragile, but blunt them in a manner that will not cause them to catch on the shavings.

The top of the wedge may be profiled in any fashion you choose, only requiring that the top be able to withstand mallet blows in blade setting. It is usual to break from the wedge shape to a plane parallel to the underside of the wedge, the break being placed above the level of the top of the stock. The position of this break is, of course, determined by the thickness chosen for the upper wedge, and is often $\frac{1}{4}$—$\frac{3}{4}$" above the position seen in Fig. 6:5. Chamfering the forward edges reduces edge marring by the mallet blows.

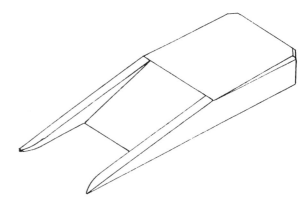

Figure 6:5

FINISHING With wedge and iron in place, the iron well retracted and wedge driven firmly home, the sole is checked for flatness. Any deviation visible under a straightedge is corrected by planing, then the bottom is further refined by rubbing on a strip of sandpaper placed on a flat surface such as a circular saw table or jointer bed. When all areas of the sole show equal sanding marks, continue with finer grades of sandpaper until the finish satisfies you.

COMPLETING THE PLANE The above description should serve for the throat formation of any bench plane you choose to make, from a one-inch violinmaker's to an eight-foot cooper's jointer. If these operations are well done, you will have a useful tool. Subsequent details allow more room for individualization, although they were rather standardized in the professional's product. The finishing touches outlined for the jack plane of the previous chapter are typical for this size plane. Others will be seen in subsequent chapters.

With these final steps completed, the iron is set properly (as described in Chapter 3) and a trial cut is made. It is not unusual to note problems, which are overcome by "fettling", as described there.

The final step, once the plane is behaving, is disassembly, final clean-up and providing the protective coating of your choice. Two hand-rubbed coats of tung or boiled linseed oil provide a minimum. An old method was to soak the plane in a barrel of raw linseed oil for a day or so, then let it stand on newspaper until it stopped draining. Another recipe was to rub in linseed oil "once a day for a week, once a week for a year, once a year for the rest of your life". Varnish was used in the declining days of wooden planemaking, and lacquer is not unknown. However, the latter two were often removed immediately after purchase of the plane by old-timers. If you have mastered the art of French polishing, this produces an exceptionally attractive finish; perhaps more suited to a display piece than a working tool. A final coat of furniture wax gives a surface attractive to many; if you choose to do so, do not wax the gripping surfaces of wedge and abutments.

COACH SMOOTH　　The small (six inch) smoothing plane illustrated in the photograph at the beginning of the chapter provides the first example of a plane made by the classical procedure. This size has been given various names: coachmaker's smooth, thumb, modeling, boy's, toy, finger, fitting, or block plane. As the last term is usually taken to mean the metal plane of this size, I prefer to avoid it.

The blade chosen was one and a quarter inches wide, of high carbon steel with matching cap iron, made especially for wooden planes by Hock. The stock to hold this began as a squared block of Honduras mahogany 6 x $2\frac{1}{8}$ x 2", the growth rings nearly parallel to the 2" sole. The bedline was scribed on the sole $2\frac{1}{4}$" back from the toe, and up each side at a 50° pitch. After completing the throat by the above procedure, the upper edges were rounded, the rear top with a larger radius to provide a comfortable grip. The front vertical edges were chamfered with a sharp chisel, stopping these with the traditional cut from a $\frac{1}{8}$" full sweep gouge. The wedge was undecorated save for rounding the top. As with all of the planes I make, it had my name embossed on the top of the toe with a classical planemaker's stamp, made for me in England.

The two smaller planes of the photograph were made in 1984, using irons acquired with a cabinetmaker's chest. The three inch long maple smoother was given the coffin shape with a bandsaw after finishing the throat. The ebony coachmaker's tailed round had its body shaped with a bandsaw, and the sole was rounded with a jack plane and scraper, to match the blade profile. All three are serviceable planes.

CHAPTER 7

JOINTER, USING CLASSICAL METHOD
(Recovering from faulty construction)

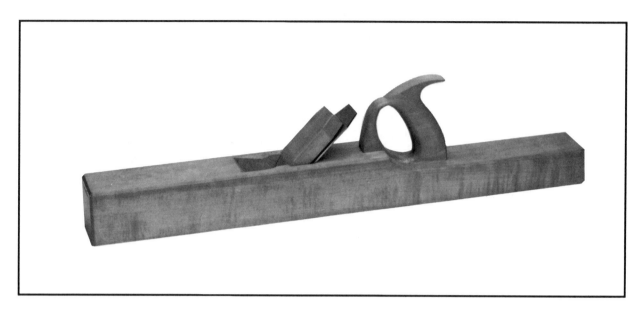

The jointer, as its name implies, is used primarily to "joint" the edges of long boards, making them perfectly flat and straight. Two jointed boards will fit together perfectly edge to edge, so that they may be glued together to form a wider board with no gaps to weaken the joint. The jointer sole must be long and perfectly flat to do this; flat because the edge will copy any curvature, long so that it will not dip into hollow places on the board's edge, but will ride over them and only cut off the high spots.

The purist may disagree with the requirement of a perfectly flat sole. In fact, it is really only necessary for three sections of the sole to be "flat" in the sense of being exactly in the same plane; one at the toe, one immediately in front of the mouth, and one near the heel. Japanese craftsman often relieve the intermediate sections of their plane soles by a "hair of light" (a very small amount) to ensure that the sole in front of the mouth presses strongly on the work. Practically, the easiest way to meet this minimum requirement is to flatten the entire sole. You will find old planes with soles scarred by collisions with nails or other obsta-

cles that still perform well — if they meet the above minimum.

My first attempt at planemaking, in 1983, was a 26½" razee jointer. I had been acquiring and using Stanley tools for some time, but had developed a yen for wooden planes. After collecting and refurbishing a goodly number of these, and finding a likely length of 3 x 3" maple left over from building my workbench, the temptation arose to try my hand at making one. To make full use of the length of maple, a jointer was called for. A flaw in the top of one end inspired the razee style. Fortunately, removal of the flaw did not conflict with the proper choice of grain orientation of the block (growth rings not too far from horizontal, grain sloping down toward the heel).

The method was adapted from the useful text of Perch and Lee (1981). Only a general description will be given, as details of layout and throat formation are available in the previous chapter. These will suffice to guide you in duplication of the plane pictured, but in your case as in mine, patterns will be modified to

36

suit the material at hand and your personal preferences.

It is a good idea to prepare a dimensioned sketch of the plane you plan to make (if you are not using an authentic plane as prototype). It is easier to change a pencil line than a half-finished plane, if you find a problem. I have seen several user-made jacks which had the tops of their irons bent over, because the tote would not let them be installed otherwise.

The block was squared to make the sides flat and perpendicular to the flat top and bottom. The razee was cut with a band saw, dropping the rear section to a two-inch height but leaving the front 15¾" at full height. The curve at the front of this cut was smoothed with a sanding drum in a drill press.

A modern style two-inch iron with a cap iron was acquired from a tool dealer. The throat was laid out and cut as described in the last chapter, placing the bed line on the sole 9" from the toe and using 45° pitch. The wedge was made from a blank ¾ x 2 x 7" and fitted, again as described in Chapter 6.

I chose to depart from the traditional closed tote (which accepts three fingers, allowing the forefinger to project forward) and make a four-finger grip. (This works, but it convinced me that the old style is better.) The profile was laid out on 1" (full) maple, allowing ⅝" to fit into the mortise in the stock (a better profile is sketched in Fig. 21:2, for the cornice plane.) The handhole was begun by boring holes at the upper and lower extremities, and the remaining material was removed with a coping saw. All edges of the tote, save the top of the spur and the part which fits into its mortise, were rounded with rasps and sanded smooth for a comfortable grip.

The front of the mortise for the tote was located 2¾" behind the bed line, determined by the need to prevent the tote from interfering with the removal of the iron. This placed it a bit over one inch forward of the start of the razee, meaning that the mortise started at the high section of the stock, continued down the razee curve and finished in the lower razee section, the total length being 4½". The front of the handhole in the tote pattern was made to parallel the curve of

the razee. The front and rear of the mortise were made square in this case, requiring the rear of the tote to remain square where it fit into its mortise. It is more conventional to use a 1" drill for the after end of the mortise and to shape the rear of the handle bottom into a semicylinder to fit. The mortise was roughed out with a Forstner bit and finished with chisels. (At that time I didn't know about end mills.) After fitting the tote and smoothing the stock, they were united with yellow glue.

The finishing touches for this plane (having already deviated from usual practice) were restricted to simple chamfers on all sharp edges save those of the sole. The tool was finished with several coats of boiled linseed oil.

Initial results with this plane were not satisfying, and it was laid aside. Years later, having learned how to adjust the iron properly and improve the fit of the cap iron (see Chapter 3), results were greatly improved, but not enough to make me choose this jointer over my Stanley No.7. The cut was rough, as the mouth opening was too wide, being more suitable for a jack plane than a jointer. This quarter inch opening was due both to using too wide a mouth in the layout, and cutting the bed more deeply than the layout line in my inexperienced struggle to obtain a flat bed. Further, the sole was no longer flat, either because I had not flattened it adequately initially or because the wood had distorted slightly over the years.

There is a remedy for these faults, however. You will often see it on a well-used old plane whose mouth has been widened by wear and sole redressing. The sole was planed flat, and a new mouth front was made by inserting an inlay in the sole.

A 2⅛" square of 3/16" rosewood was prepared, with the edge that was to become the new mouth front (an end grain edge) beveled at the 75° slope of the old lower throat front. With the iron wedged in place, the patch was placed on the sole, its beveled edge at the position of the iron's cutting edge. The outline of the patch was scribed with a sharp marking knife. The scribe marks were deepened with a chisel, then a depression was cut into the sole to just under the thickness of the patch. I used an end mill and a drill press cross vise to sink the recess to the proper depth (in the manner described at the end of the chapter) and finished the corners with a Stanley #271 hand router and a chisel. You might prefer to outline the recess with a paring chisel and sink it with a gouge and the router. With a tight fit obtained, the patch was glued in place and planed to the level of the original sole (with the polishing smooth plane of Chapter 4). Sole flatness was insured by rubbing it on sandpaper placed on the circular saw table, after which the linseed oil finish was replaced.

The new mouth opening was a bit too small, and it was opened out carefully with a thin flat file. The performance of the jointer is now fine. The mouth was left small, as in the polishing smooth plane, and the tool will choke if too heavy a cut is taken; but the cut is very smooth. This is now the jointer of choice in my shop.

USING AN END MILL The metalworker's end mills can be very useful tools for the woodworker; some applications have been reviewed recently (Beck 1993). Shaped roughly like a drill bit, they have a flat bottom carrying cutting edges, and spiral flutes on the sides also with very sharp cutting edges (handle them with care!). A quarter-inch mill will do any of the tasks reported here, although an assortment of larger sizes will do some of them faster. They are available from many machine shop supply sources, local or through mail order. Avoid the "double ended" type, which can be mounted in a milling machine to use either end, but will not serve in a drill press chuck.

In planemaking, they are useful for cutting recesses for inlay (as the mouth patch above) or to inlay metal fittings such as depth stop feet or bearing plates. You will find them used to start certain plane beds, in later chapters. For these applications, they are particularly useful simply chucked in a drill press and used in conjunction with a drill press cross vise (also called a compound vise). These, (Fig. 7:1), are available inexpensively from a number of mail order

houses. The cross vise is a machinist's vise mounted on two cross-slides, capable of moving the vise precisely in either of two directions at right angles to each other. The vise holds the work rigidly while the mill is cutting, either plunging or traversing.

The vise is screwed firmly to the drill press table, using bolts through the table's slots. The workpiece is clamped in the vise, positioned so that the area to be cut is within the travel range of the two traverse screws of the crossheads. Don't forget to secure the table firmly to the post of the press; traversing the mill can build up significant sidewise thrust. A large workpiece such as the above jointer, which won't fit in the vise, is simply clamped to a smaller block of wood that is held in the vise jaws. In either case, make sure that the bottom of the cut you wish to make is exactly parallel to the table surface.

Figure 7:1

Set the depth stop of the drill press to prevent the mill from cutting below the desired level. Start the cut as if you were drilling. Some end mills are not center cutting. These will stop cutting when their centers hit the wood surface, and must be raised and traversed to remove the uncut core. (Center-cutting mills are available, and should be preferred.) The mill will cut either while plunging or while traversing, but in the present application works better if you remove the bulk of the waste by a series of plunges, then traverse the mill for the final cut. (Do NOT attempt to traverse with the mill unless the workpiece is held rigidly in the cross vise!) Assuming the rectangular outline to be cut is mounted parallel to the cross-slide direction, the mill will follow its sides accurately (save for the round corners) simply by operating the traversing screws one at a time. Once set at the scribe mark, the cutter will traverse exactly along the line. When the perimeter is completed, the interior is easily removed by the same process. By keeping the drill press quill at the limit set by its depth stop, an exact depth of cut is obtained. Comparable accuracy with a power router would require building a jig to limit its path.

The round corners of the recess are easily squared with chisel and hand router.

The combination of end mill and cross vise is but one of the ways a recess may be produced. The professional planemakers (and perhaps some professional woodworkers today) could probably accomplish the same cut as precisely in even less time, with hand tools alone. One without their high level of skill can equal the precision of their work by use of this technique.

CHAPTER 8

BULLNOSE PLANE

Occasionally a circumstance arises where a surface must be smoothed up to an internal corner or some other obstacle; one that interferes with the nose of the plane and prevents completion of the plane's stroke. An example is seen in smoothing the under side of the arms of the wedge-arm plane of Chapter 16. There is a tool called an edge plane which can be used in these cases, one of which is seen at A on the left of Fig. 8:1. It has the cutting edge at the very front of the stock, with no front to its mouth. The lack of downward pressure on the wood in front of the cut can lead to a rough planed surface.

A more common expedient is to allow a very short span of sole in front of the mouth. Such tools are called bullnose planes. Since wood is not strong enough (especially in the short grain involved) to permit short spans, they normally have the throat front made of brass. Two variants of these are shown at B and C in Fig. 8:1. Usually small, they are handy for many uses that might otherwise be served by a metal block plane. They are particularly useful in cutting "stopped" chamfers, where the chamfer is terminated before reaching the end of the edge being softened.

The applewood plane illustrated uses as a prototype one made by William Chapple (Manchester 1876-81), and makes use of an iron acquired in a batch of flea market hardware. This measures $1\frac{5}{8}$ x $4\frac{1}{2}$" and is uncut (that is, without the slot for a cap iron). It is marked Stanley Rule and Level Co. on the bevel side, and is apparently originally from a low angle metal block plane.

A block of hardwood five inches long is squared to $2\frac{1}{2}$" high x $2\frac{3}{8}$" wide. The face chosen as the toe (from criteria in Chapter 1) is cut to slant back from the sole at an angle of 80°. The throat is to be shaped in the same basic design as described in Chapter 6, but is considerably easier to cut as the bed surface is more accessible. Most of the bed can be cut with a power tool, working through the open front of the throat.

I mounted the blank in a drill press cross vise with the sole at 45°, and cut the center section of the bed ($1\frac{1}{4}$" wide) with an end mill, using the procedure

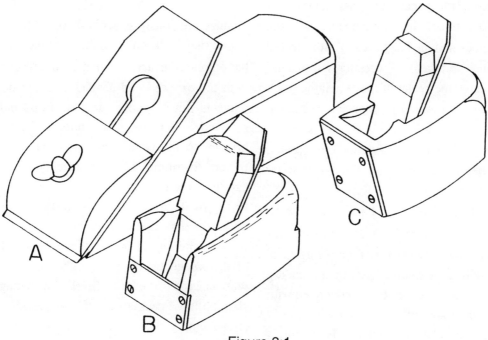

Figure 8:1

described at the end of Chapter 7. An alternate method is to mount the blank in a jig, sole up at 45°, and make the cut on a table saw. Use either a dado head or nibbling with the normal blade. Either of these methods removes a significant amount of wood. Proceed slowly, not removing too much with any one pass of the cutter. Haste is hazardous not only to the tool, but to you! For the hand tool purist, saws and chisels will serve. The depth of cut is chosen to make the bed surface intersect the sole just $\frac{3}{16}$" back of the toe. The stock at this stage is shown in Fig. 8:2.

With this much of the throat open, the procedure of Chapter 6 is resumed. The bed is widened by saw cuts guided by the original bed surface. These cuts (made with allowance of a margin for final paring) bring the bed surface to its final width of $1\frac{3}{4}$". Two more cuts with a detail or knife saw define the abutment surfaces, sloping back from the toe at 55°. Chisel away the waste between these cuts and the cuts extending the bed, and carefully pare flat both bed and abutments to produce the shape shown in Fig. 8:3. Finish with a float if you have one, files if you do not. The open top front of the throat is pared to produce eyes.

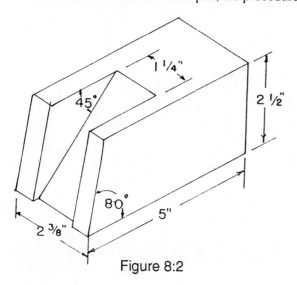

Figure 8:2

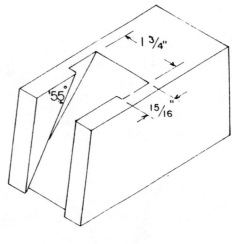

Figure 8:3

41

The bullnose front is cut from brass plate (I used 11 gauge, .091" thick). Its width matches the toe width of the stock and the height is $1\frac{1}{2}$". It is drilled and countersunk to take 4 #4 woodscrews, placing the holes to match the center of the remaining stock sides. The lower screws must not penetrate into the wedge slot ($\frac{1}{2}$" above the sole served for $\frac{1}{2}$" screws). The lower edge of the brass plate should be located very slightly below the level of the sole, to allow for adjustment after mounting.

The heel of the plane is cut back to $1\frac{1}{2}$" width with arcs starting $1\frac{1}{2}$" from the heel, and the top rear of the stock is rounded with a rasp for a comfortable grip. After sanding, the sharp edges of the stock top are softened with a plane, and this is continued with a chisel down the four vertical edges to the level of the top of the brass plate, terminating the chamfers with gouge cuts. The wedge is made and fitted in the manner previously described (pp.33-34). A strike button may be installed in the heel; the plane shown has one cut from a half inch of $\frac{3}{4}$" diameter brass rod, with the exposed end shaped as a flat dome. The plane is finish sanded, and the brass bullnose is screwed into place. The bottom of this plate is brought to the exact angle and level of the sole bottom, by initial filing if necessary (being very careful not to raise the bottom above sole level) and finally by the usual procedure of flattening the sole on a strip of sandpaper on a flat surface.

After honing the iron and some minor adjustment of the wedge fit, the plane behaved well (for one without a cap iron). It was finished with tung oil. The short bullnose causes a bit of a problem in starting a stroke, until you get used to it.

CHAPTER 9

BOXMAKER'S PLANE
An example of a low angle plane

In the days before cardboard cartons, many goods were shipped in wooden boxes. These were built for durability under shipping conditions, and were intended to last for many round trips. Their appearance was secondary. The tradesmen called boxmakers supplied this need.

Rough sawn planks needed only enough surface planing to remove the worst of the saw marks. This was done with a plane resembling a smooth plane, but with a low bed angle and a wide mouth. Salaman (1975) reports the name "flogger" for this tool.

Not having found an authentic one as prototype, the applewood plane pictured was made based on the drawing and description in his text. A modern two inch double iron was used (although undoubtedly single irons were more usual).

LAYOUT As shown in Fig. 9:1, square a blank 9 x 2⅝ x 2⅝" and locate the bed line 2½" back of the toe on the sole. Lay out the side bed lines at 35°.

A wide mouth is used to accommodate the rough cutting, placing the mouth line ⅜" in front of the bed line on the sole. The top bedline is squared across the top joining the ends of the side bed lines, and the front of the throat is scribed 3⅞" forward of this. Because of the low pitch, the abutment line is placed 1½" in front of the top bedline. Except for these dimension changes, the

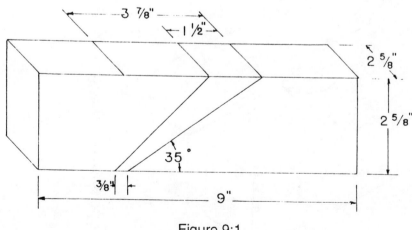

Figure 9:1

changes, the layout follows the procedure given in Chapter 6, and subsequent cutting can follow the same sequence.

THROAT As is true of all of the planes in this volume, the throat can be cut entirely by hand, without power tools, using only chisels. This one in particular, however, benefits from application of a machinist's end mill. The top $3\frac{1}{4}$" of the $4\frac{1}{2}$" bed is accessible to this tool because of the low pitch, and this provides a convenient way to start the throat (much as was done with the bullnose plane). This effortlessly produces a perfectly flat surface over a significant fraction of the bed area. A cross vise screwed to the drill press table holds the stock rigidly, at the proper angle (35° to the table), and traverses it under the mill chucked in the drill press under complete control (details of the procedure are given on p.38). The cut, as in the earlier description, is restricted to a width $\frac{7}{16}$" less than the width of your iron.

Having gained this head start, the procedure returns to the standard sequence previously described in Chapter 6. After drilling through from the mouth, the bed surface is extended downward with chisels and floats or files. The machined surface aids greatly in this operation. Cut the abutments, widen the throat and cut the eyes as previously described. The end mill can be again called into service to cut the clearance slot for the cap iron screw.

STOCK SHAPING The rounded shape, similar to the usual smooth plane "coffin" pattern, is sawn out with bandsaw or turning saw, narrowing the toe to $1\frac{7}{8}$" and the heel to $1\frac{1}{2}$". Round the upper rear of the stock for the hand grip, and chamfer the plane to your preference. The illustration uses narrow ($\frac{3}{16}$") chamfers carried down the sides and stopped with gouge cuts $1\frac{1}{4}$" above the sole. A hardwood strike button installed in the heel of the plane protects it from mallet damage in setting the blade.

MITER PLANE Two typical American miter planes are shown in Fig. 9:2, the one on the left in the common "coffin" shape, the other one square. The only differences between these planes and the flogger described above is that the former have even lower pitches, tighter mouths and are not quite so high. A coffin miter plane in my collection by John Veit (1857-99) is pitched at 32° and is 2" high, $2\frac{7}{8}$" wide and $10\frac{1}{2}$" long; it uses a single iron. The above description should serve to reproduce either of the miter planes shown, with dimensions changed to match those of a prototype you wish to duplicate. The lower pitch of these planes creates an area intolerant of careless chisel work, the acute angle at the rear of the mouth. The iron chosen for any low angle plane must be ground at an angle that is more acute than the pitch of the bed (except for certain metal soled planes equipped with bevel-up irons).

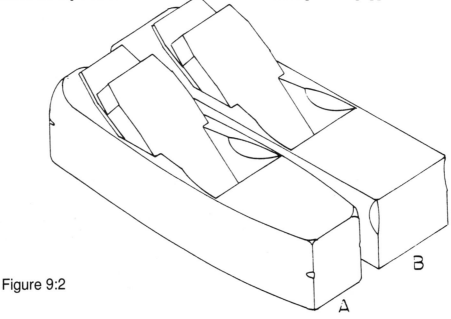

Figure 9:2

44

CHAPTER 10

STOP CHAMFER PLANE

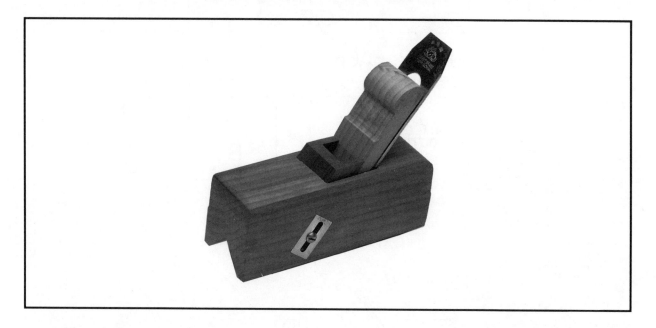

"Arris" is a very useful word which has unfortunately dropped out of common usage. It refers to the sharp edge formed where two surfaces meet. This is properly called an "edge" today, but the word "edge" is also used to refer to the smaller of the surfaces of a board, as the "side edge" or "front edge". This can lead to confusion. A board has an arris where its face and one of its "edges" meet, to form a sharp corner. Let's use the word "arris" here to refer to this line, and restrict "edge" to mean a surface.

Because an arris is sharp and uncomfortable to hold or bump against, it is often relieved by planing it away. It is either rounded, or softened by forming a small flat surface at an angle to both of the original surfaces. This is called a chamfer, and the chamfer plane is a convenient way to cut it.

The most often seen chamfer plane is called the Mander and Dillin type, as James Mander patented it in this country (U.S. 314338, 24 Mar. 1885, assigning one third to Maurice R. Dillin) and it was produced by the partnership Mander and Dillin. The chamfer width is controlled by the setting of a stop in the throat, whence the name "stop chamfer plane". This

should not be confused with a stop chamfer, which refers to a chamfer that terminates before the end of the arris (such as the vertical chamfers on many planes). This type of chamfer plane is more often seen with British makers' marks, and Mander (a British citizen) may have brought the design to this country with him.

The stop (seen in Fig.10:1D) slides in a mortise through the body of the plane (Fig.10:2). The mortise forms a rectangular opening which is completely filled by the stop, wedge and iron, leaving only the throat formed by hollowing the back of the stop. The rear of this mortise serves as the bed of the plane. The flat bottom of the stop serves as the sole, in contact with the chamfer being cut. The rear bottom of the stop serves as the front of the mouth, pressing on the chamfer in front of the cutting edge of the iron. The stop is adjusted up or down until the distance between the two angled sides of the stock, measured along the flat bottom of the stop, is equal to the width of the chamfer to be cut.

Having set the position of the stop for the desired chamfer width, it is secured in position by the screw

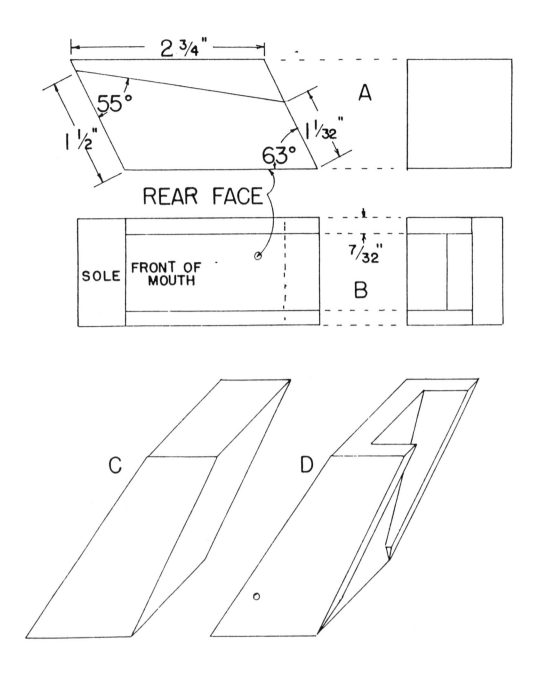

REAR FACE

2 ¾"

55°

1 ½"

63°

1 1/32"

A

SOLE | FRONT OF MOUTH

7/32"

B

C

D

Figure 10:1

through the side of the stock. This plane is held at a 45° angle, the left side of its V-bottom pressed against the side of the work. Planing is continued until the right side of the V reaches the top of the work, stopping the cut.

The applewood plane of the photograph is now in the collection of Frank Lemoine, who has my thanks for permitting it to be photographed. The prototype for its construction was made by Griffiths,

Norwich. The replica begins with a squared block 6¾ x 2¼ x 2½" high and an iron 1½" wide. I chose to use a 1½" iron with a cap iron, although my prototype and most chamfer planes use single irons. The mortise is laid out as a rectangle on the top of the stock 1½" wide and 1⅞" long, centered in the width and 2" from the heel. The bed lines on the sides of the stock are scribed at 55°, and the layout line for the front of the mortise is scribed at the same angle. The waste is

46

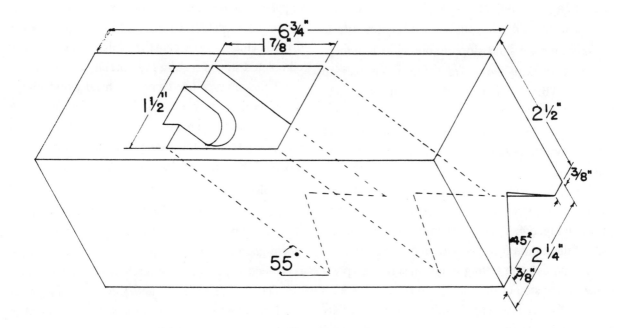

Figure 10:2

drilled and sawn away with a keyhole saw, and the four surfaces are pared to flatness. Remember that the rear serves as the bed for the iron, and recall the cautions about keeping this surface flat in the cutting of a conventional throat. The sole is V-notched by two 45° cuts of the table saw, leaving ⅜" of sole untouched on either side. The rear of the mortise is grooved to clear the head of the screw that holds the cutting iron and cap iron together, as we have seen several times in earlier chapters. The stock at this point is shown in Fig. 10:2, with its mortise of uniform rectangular cross-section indicated by dotted lines.

A slot for the stop adjustment screw is to be cut through a cheek of the stock. English planes use one screw, either on the left or right side (I chose the left side, rather than the prototype's right). Mander and Dillin used two, one on each side. The screw slot is ¾" long and ¼" wide, parallel to the front of the mortise through the stock and ⅛" away from it. The lower corner of this slot is ¾" above the sole. Begin by drilling ¼" holes and join them with chisel cuts.

The front of the effective throat is formed in the sole box (stop), the cutting of which is shown in Fig.

10:1. Start with stock squared to 1½ x 1½", long enough for safe handling on the table saw, and cut one end at 63°. (A table saw with blade vertical and miter gage set accurately at 27° is recommended.) Measure 1¹⁄₃₂" along this cut from the acute angle, and mark this point. Scribe a line parallel to the angle cut, at 63° to the side and 2¾" away from the cut. Measure 1½" along this line and mark a second point. Join the two points with a line. Using a taper guide, cut along this line to form the surface which will become the front of the stop. Cut off the stop blank, again with the miter gauge set at 27°, along the remaining scribe line. These measurements establish the required 55° angle between front and bottom of the stop, while keeping the wood grain parallel to its rear face. The piece, in the orientation seen in Fig. 10:1C, should fit snugly into the front end of the mortise in the stock, its ends aligned with stock top and bottom. The stock may require paring to allow this. With the stop in place, its lower rear edge will become the mouth front.

The rear of this sliding stop will provide the abutment surfaces which hold the wedge. Call this the rear face. The center of this is to be cut away to

47

provide an exit for shavings (corresponding to the throat in a bench plane). Scribe abutment lines $\frac{7}{32}$" in from the long edges on this face, and continue these for $\frac{5}{8}$" along the short slope adjoining it. Join them with a line marking the top front of the throat, as seen in Fig. 10:1B. Saw along the abutment lines down to this last line, but do not allow the cut to go beyond the mouth at the other end. The triangular wedge of waste between these saw cuts is now removed with chisels.

The lower ends of the abutments must be removed in the same fashion as in a classical mouth, as shown in Fig. 6:4. They are cut away on a slant to the ends of the mouth front, as seen in Fig. 10:1D.

The adjustment setting screw must now be positioned in the side of the sliding stop. Insert the stop with its front held tightly against the front of its mortise. Slide it upward until its bottom is at the level of the peak of the V in the bottom of the stock. Make a mark on the side of the stop at the location of the upper end of the slot in the stock that will admit this screw. This locates the position of the pilot hole to be drilled in the stop to accept the adjustment screw. The completed stop is seen in Fig. 10:1D.

The prototype used a cheese-head wood adjustment screw, which may be hard to find today. A fillister head or even a round will serve. The head of the setting screw should bear on metal, to protect the wood of the stock. A $\frac{5}{8}$ x 1" rectangle is cut from brass plate, and a rectangular slot is made in this $\frac{3}{4}$" long and wide enough for easy travel of the screw shank. The plate is inlet into the side of the stock, its slot aligned with the previously cut screw slot. There is no need to affix it, as the screw will keep it in place.

The wedge is made and fitted, and the other finishing touches applied in the same manner as in any bench plane (as in Chapter 5).

CHAPTER 11

SPILL PLANE

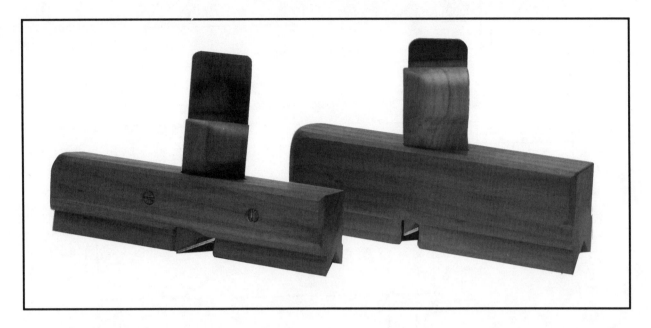

In the days before matches, a means of carrying a flame from the hearth to light a candle or a pipe was a necessity. A curled wood shaving called a spill was the usual means. Collectors of pattern glass will recognize a certain design of glassware (also called a "spill") used in the homes of the middle 1800's to hold these lighters.

Many woodworker's kits contained a plane used to convert scraps of wood into spills. Unlike the present day throw-away mentality, one was expected to find uses for odds and ends of left-over wood, and this was a popular one. The housewife would appreciate them, and a handful might even be worth a beer at the local inn. The spill planes were usually made by their owner; few have a maker's stamp. Many styles have been observed, sharing only the characteristic of a sharply skewed cutting edge which produces the desired curled shaving. Several are depicted in the useful *Dictionary of Tools* (Salaman 1975), including one quite similar to the prototype

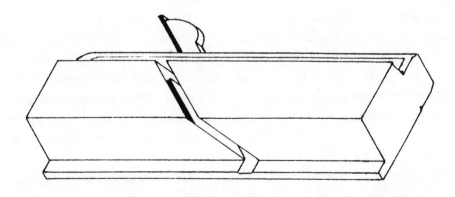

Figure 11:1

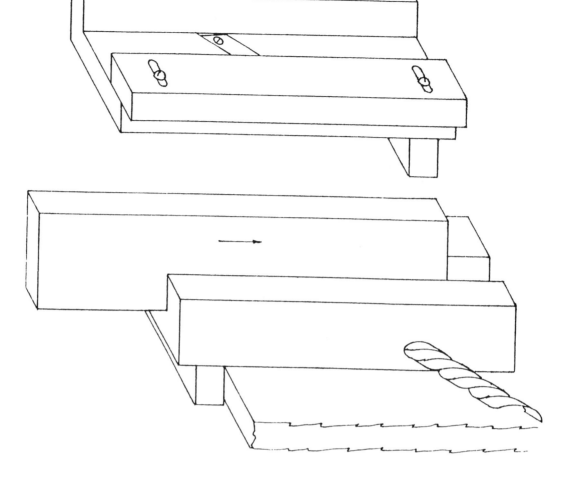

Figure 11:2

used for the planes of the photograph. Another is seen in Fig. 11:1. While most are hand held, some are designed to be mounted on a bench with the wood moved over them. One such is shown in Fig.11:2; the lower view shows it in use with the spill emerging from a hole in its side.

Spill planes appear, albeit rather infrequently, at tool auctions or swap sessions. Acquiring these as tools to be used is a bit of a gamble. I own several that just cannot be made to work properly, and other collectors have found the same. The suspicion is that these were made in an idle moment by someone, based on a faulty recollection of one that had been seen in use. Having been made and found not to work, they were put on a shelf to fix "someday" and survived the maker. Most, however, yield to enough tinkering and will produce spills.

The prototype used here was acquired at an English tool auction, and was found to work well (although it appears venerable enough to have earned retirement). Another in my collection, of the same general design but crudely made, also produces spills.

The applewood planes of the photograph heading this chapter represent two types of construction. One copied the prototype as closely as possible, in the classical one-piece construction. It is now in the collection of Frank Lemoine, who has my thanks for allowing it to be photographed. The second was made by an adaptation of the French style, an open throat closed by a batten.

Although the blade stands upright in the stock, the combination of a sharp skew angle (65°, or 25° off the front-to-back center line) and the sloping sole

50

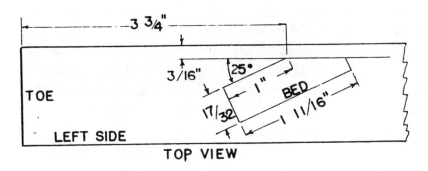

TOE

LEFT SIDE

TOP VIEW

Figure 11:3

(V-notched at 45° to the sides) produces an effective pitch of 33°. The wedge is designed to provide the equivalent of a chip breaker, providing a slanting surface just above the cutting edge of the iron to start the curl of the spill.

The skew blade required for this project will be hard to find. An old spill plane with a badly damaged stock might be found, or a skew iron from another type of plane might be ground down. If the latter is an old one, be sure not to grind beyond the steel part of the iron. Even a modern bench plane iron will serve, if you cut away the skew without getting it hot enough to lose its temper. You may see recently made spill planes with blades improvised from saw or scraper blades; these are too thin to work well. The easiest course is to make your own; the procedure used for the above planes is outlined below.

BLADE   For both versions, the blade is made from a five inch length of $\frac{1}{8}$ x $1\frac{1}{2}$" ground flat stock of oil hardening steel (O-1); water hardening steel such as W-1 will also serve. The lower end is cut (hacksawn) at an angle of 65° to the side, and the corners of the upper end rounded. With the blade flat on the bench and the acute point on the top left, the bevel is to be formed on the side facing up. Start forming this with a file, but do not complete the sharpening. A blunt edge is left, as a sharp edge might suffer from the hardening and tempering procedure to be used. This is effected as described on p.115, with the exception that temper is drawn only to the light straw stage. The edge is then ground and honed.

Even more than is the case with other planes, only a truly keen edge will produce satisfactory results.

STOCK   The copy of the prototype begins as a squared blank of hardwood $7\frac{7}{8}$ x $2\frac{1}{2}$ x $1\frac{3}{8}$". In contrast to most planes, the effective sole is at an angle of 45° to the sides of the stock. The preferred orientation of the annual rings is parallel to the sole, which means that they lie at 45° to the plane sides.

LAYOUT   The shape of the wedge and wedge mortise is most unconventional. It is easy to lose track of toe and heel in the layout and cutting, and it is prudent to label one or the other in pencil. The wedge angle is almost imperceptible. Some of the dimensions may sound unduly accurate, but these are as measured, and are necessary for proper wedge fitting. The top layout is sketched in Fig. 11:3.

The front of the wedge (and its mortise) is beveled back on its right side. The location of this bevel is marked on the top of the stock with a line parallel to the right side of the stock and $\frac{3}{16}$" away from it. (You will recall that the right side of the stock is on your right as you face the rear of the plane.) From a point on this line $3\frac{3}{4}$" from the toe scribe another line running forward and to the left at an angle of 25° to the side of the stock, for a distance of one inch. This marks the front of the mortise. From the forward end of the mortise front, turn left at a right angle to mark the side of the mortise (at an angle of 65° to the side of the stock) and mark a line $\frac{17}{32}$" long for the forward side. Continue from the left end of this with another right angle turn and scribe the line marking the rear of the mortise, $1\frac{11}{16}$" long and parallel to the mortise front. Another right angle turn from the heel end of this line returns you to the original line.

The mortise is to be sunk at right angles to the top of the stock, except for the slight inward taper of the front and bevel surfaces. Guide lines for this are

51

provided by lightly sketching in lines at right angles to the sides from the five corners of the mortise outline and dropping perpendicular lines down both sides from the ends of these.

CUTTING THE WEDGE MORTISE   The bulk of the waste between the layout lines on the top is removed by drilling through to the sole. A drill press helps greatly in keeping these holes perpendicular to the top. Holes on the right side of the stock had better be stopped short of breaking through to avoid splintering, but the others break through into wood that will be removed later.

Continue clearing the waste with a mortise chisel, and finish with paring chisels. A narrow ($\frac{1}{8}$") chisel will be needed for the short side, and a pair of skew chisels is useful. If a float (p.61) is available, it is of great help, but files and sanding sticks will serve. The front of the mortise is to have a slight taper, narrowing the distance between it and the rear wall at the very bottom of the cut to $\frac{15}{32}$". This will require a similar slight taper to the bevel side of the mortise as well.

COMPLETING THE STOCK   The bottom of the stock is to be cut away in a V by two sawcuts at 45° to the sides. Scribe 45° lines on toe and heel, beginning at $\frac{3}{16}$" from the right edge of the bottom of the stock blank. Measure in one inch from the bottom along these lines, and strike the lines for the other side of the V back to the left side of the stock. The lower right side of the stock is to be rabbeted away for $\frac{5}{8}$" above the bottom and $\frac{1}{8}$" deep. The outline for this is marked on the ends. The heel view of this layout is seen in Fig. 11:4.

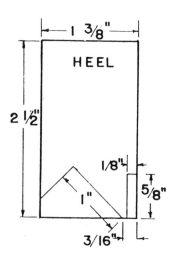

Figure 11:4

With a carefully set circular saw, make the cut for the right side of the V, the kerf inside the mark. Defer making the other 45° cut until the rabbet is formed, to retain the bottom of the block for the rabbet cut. This is made with the blade vertical, the stock upright and its left side against the fence. The other 45° cut now completes the V-notch. Finally (if your sawblade cut is less than $\frac{1}{8}$" thick), lay the stock on its side and make the cut completing the rabbet.

The inward step above the rabbet on the right side of the sole is softened by coving with a small hollow plane. The exit for the spills is created by removing the $\frac{1}{16}$" wall remaining between the wedge mortise and the rabbet. Pare back the edges of this opening to allow for smooth shavings exit. A portion of the area above this exit, above the cove, is pared away for the same purpose.

This completes the stock, with the exception of the usual trim of rounding the top rear for comfortable holding, chamfering top arrises and stop chamfering the vertical ones.

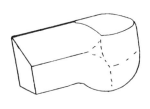

Figure 11:5

WEDGE   Because of the very small taper used in the mortise and the wedge shape, fitting the wedge to the mortise is more difficult than usual. Begin with a blank 1 x $1\frac{11}{16}$ x 5" or longer and reduce all but the upper $1\frac{1}{2}$" to a thickness of a bit over $\frac{7}{16}$". Profile the wedge (shown in Fig. 11:5) to match the cross-section of the mortise, with paring chisels. With the iron in place, adjust the fit carefully until the iron seats solidly with a light tap on the wedge top. Because of the interference of the material for the wedge finial, this is difficult to achieve with a plane; a hand scraper is more effective.

Set the iron in position, its cutting edge at the level of the wide side of the sole V, and seat the wedge with a mallet blow. Scribe the position of the iron's cutting edge on the wedge. Remove the wedge and cut away its lower end just above the scribe mark, angling upward at about 45°. This provides the chip breaker action to curl the shaving. (A hollow surface is sometimes seen here in similar planes, helping to curl the spill but also weakening the bottom of the wedge.) Finish the wedge finial to a profile of your choice.

TWO-PIECE CONSTRUCTION This second example was made slightly smaller than the prototype. In the two-piece method, most of the wedge mortise is accessible for sawing rather than chiseling. The blank is squared to 1 x 2 x 8".

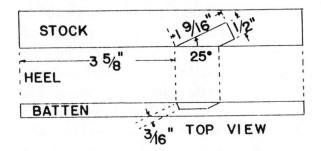

Figure 11:6

LAYOUT The bed line (marking the surface which will support the blade) is scribed vertically on the right side, $3\frac{5}{8}$" from the heel. It is continued over the top and the bottom at the skew angle, slanting forward at 25° from the side. A top view of the layout is seen in Fig. 11:6. The line locating the mortise front is scribed parallel to the bed line on the top of the blank and $\frac{1}{2}$" away from it toward the toe, and the corresponding line is scribed across the bottom $\frac{7}{16}$" away from the bed line. A line is placed on the right side joining the two points at which these lines meet the side.

The forward narrow side of the wedge mortise is located by measuring $1\frac{9}{16}$" along the bed line, from the right side of the stock, and scribed at right angles to the bed line on both top and bottom of the blank. (The other side of the wedge mortise will be formed in the batten.)

The waste between these lines may be removed easily, beginning with saw cuts along bed and front lines (leaving margin for paring) and continuing with a mortise chisel. Pare these surfaces, making the bed truly flat.

The V-notch in the sole may now be cut on the table saw, with blade set at 45°. With the stock placed on its right side on the saw table, cut into the right side of the stock to a depth (along the cut) of $\frac{3}{4}$", leaving a sharp arris at the bottom. Meet this with another cut at right angles to the first. The stock at this stage is seen at the top of Fig. 11:7.

BATTEN The batten is squared to $\frac{3}{8}$ x $\frac{7}{8}$ x 8". (Appearance of the plane is improved if the batten and stock are both sawn from the same 8" length of wide stock.) As the glue joint to the stock is to be reinforced with screws, it is convenient to drill and countersink the batten for #10 screws now, and screw the batten temporarily to the right side of the stock, flush with its top, for layout.

The skew line on the top of the stock marking the front of the mortise is extended across the batten, as shown at the bottom of Fig. 11:6. At the point where the bedline meets the batten, a line at right angles to the bedline is scribed on the top of the batten for a distance of $\frac{3}{16}$". From the end of this, a line is scribed forward parallel to the batten side until it meets the

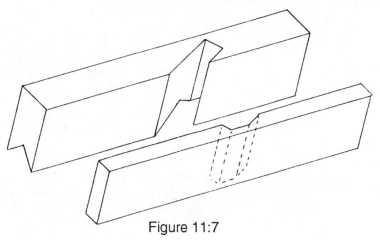

Figure 11:7

53

line marking the front of the mortise. The process is repeated on the bottom of the batten, making the measurement on the heel side of the mortise $\frac{1}{32}$" smaller ($\frac{5}{32}$"). The batten is now unscrewed from the stock, and the wedge mortise is completed by wasting the wood between these lines and paring to flat surfaces. The short section parallel to the side of the batten and the mortise front are given very slight tapers, as in the one-piece case.

The lower side of the batten may now be molded to your preference, an ogee being used here. It is then glued and screwed to the stock. The making and fitting of the wedge are carried out in the same manner as described above.

FINISHING   After finish scraping and sanding, the top and vertical arrises of the plane are chamfered, terminating those on the left side with gouge cuts a half inch from the bottom. The lower edge of the batten is pared away a bit above the section where the wedge protrudes, to provide better clearance for the spills. Your choice of coating (tung oil was used for the planes shown) completes the plane.

USING SPILL PLANES   In making spills, the setting of the iron is critical to success. Begin with the finest possible setting of the iron, the exposure of the cutting edge uniform and barely visible when sighting along the sole. The bottom of the wedge should be a uniform $\frac{1}{16}$" or less above the cutting edge. A short (about 8") piece of softwood $\frac{3}{4}$" or less in thickness is held edge up in a vise, with attention to the grain direction. The plane is held with its sides at a 45° angle, making the V sole fit the edge and left side of the workpiece. The planing stroke is very rapid. If the cut tries to stall before the end of the stroke, decrease the iron exposure. If the cutting edge exposure is not uniform, the first spills will be acceptable but after cutting several of them the edge of the workpiece will develop an angle and will need jointing. Once the correct setting of the plane is found, hundreds of spills can be made in a few minutes.

Both planes worked very well when first made (in the summer). However, they are temperamental and refused initially to come to a proper setting in wintertime. The small taper magnifies the small thickness change as the wood dries in the low humidity of winter, and the wedge moves downward beyond the cutting edge. This can be corrected with shims of paper on the forward surface of the wedge, but setting is even more time-consuming. A more permanent solution is refitting the wedge in winter, and allowing the wedge bottom to move upward from the cutting edge in summer. A slightly greater taper to the wedge and mortise might alleviate this problem, and was observed in the second old plane of the same design that was mentioned above.

CHAPTER 12

SIDE ESCAPEMENT PLANES
HOLLOW AND ROUND

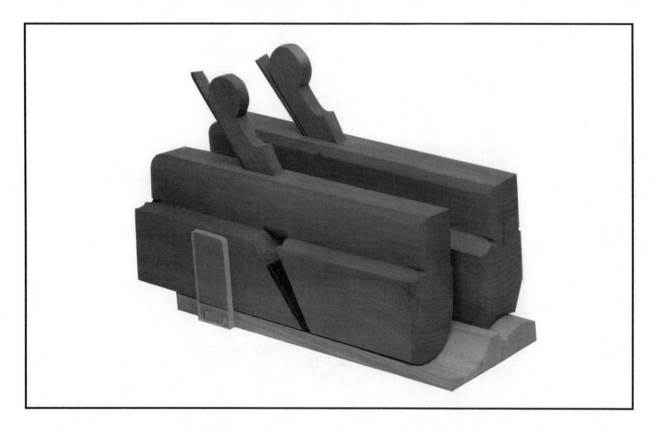

Previous chapters have described the making of the so-called bench planes, which have an open throat that allows shavings to escape through the top of the stock. The other major type of wooden plane has a wedge mortise which is completely filled by the wedge and iron, and an opening in the lower side of the tool for shavings escape. You will often hear this type called "molding planes", as a means of differentiation from the bench type. This can be misleading, as there are large molding planes which use the bench type structure, and there are shaping planes (for example, the dado of Chapter 15) made in this side opening style. The term "side escapement" is more descriptive.

Making a side escapement plane requires a rather different method of fabrication than the bench type.

Such a plane is sketched in Fig. 12:1, which provides a key to the names of its various parts.

Hollows and rounds are found more often in antique tool sources than any other planes. If your only objective is simply to acquire these, buying and restoring them is the easiest way. Making them provides a good introduction to making the side escapement type, and spurs appreciation of the ability of the old makers.

The procedure outlined here produces a pair of planes which cut a hollow and a round, each a curved surface of radius $1\frac{1}{4}$". The width dimensions may be changed, following the guidelines given by Armour and cited on pp.11-12, for pairs of other sizes. Several other dimensions are not critical. Having a pair of professionally made planes to copy is most helpful at

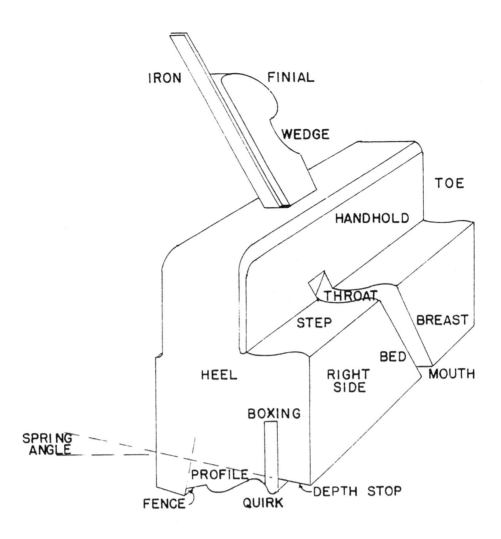

IRON FINIAL

WEDGE

TOE

HANDHOLD

THROAT

STEP BREAST

BED

HEEL RIGHT MOUTH
SIDE

BOXING

SPRING
ANGLE

PROFILE DEPTH STOP

FENCE QUIRK

Figure 12:1

many points. If these are available, you would be wise to use them as prototypes and copy their dimensions. Except for a few stylistic changes, the planes pictured were copied from a pair made by the Taber Plane Co. in New Bedford, Mass. between 1866 and 1872; their size #18.

STOCKS Two blocks of wood - beech is the usual choice - are squared to 9½" x 3½" x 1⅝". Ideally these blocks are from a slab cut through the the center of the tree, making the growth rings roughly parallel to the sole of the plane. (After much searching, I was able to acquire such a center slab from a custom cut log, one that had been well air dried.) You will find that this orientation is usually observed in the old hollow and round pairs, while other molding shapes may violate it. As in the case

of the bench planes, the grain orientation of the block is chosen which places the sole on the part of the block that was nearest to the bark in the tree, and which puts the toe on the end from which the grain slopes downward.

MARKING OUT The heel view of both stocks, showing layout lines, is seen in Fig. 12:2; the future wedge mortise is shown in dotted lines. The top of the stock is to be reduced in width to form the handhold, by cutting away to form a rabbet on the right side. The handhold width is marked at 1⅛" from the left side of the stock (the side on your left as you look at the heel). This allows for a wedge mortise ⅜" wide located in the middle third of the handhold. The position of the step at the bottom of the rabbet is

56

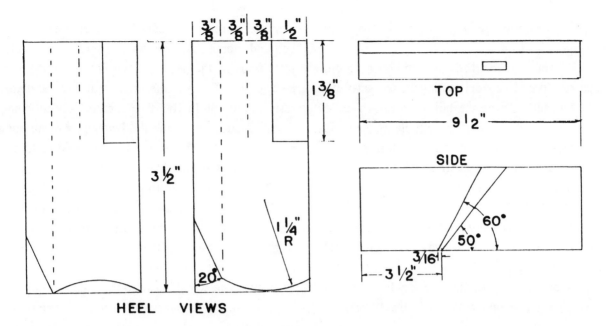

Figure 12:2

marked on heel and toe at $1\frac{3}{8}$" down from the top. The sole profile is scribed on the toe and heel of the stock. Use a template covering one-sixth of a circle of radius $1\frac{1}{4}$". Make both ends of the arc the same height, and position the end of the curve on the right side of the stock. The bevel on the lower left side is marked to begin at the extreme of the sole profile, sloping up at 20°. The left side of the sole profile should fall directly below the left side of the wedge mortise—in the present case, $\frac{3}{8}$" from the left side.

The sole bed line is marked across the sole of the stock at right angles to the sides, $3\frac{1}{2}$" from the toe. The front of the mouth is marked $\frac{3}{16}$" in front of this. Bed lines are marked on both sides of the stock, starting from the ends of the bed line on the sole and sloping up and back at 50°. These two lines are joined with a line across the top of the stock, which marks the rear of the wedge mortise. The mouth line on the sole is similarly continued up both sides at an angle of 60°, and these two lines are joined with another across the top to mark the front of the wedge mortise. The sides of this mortise are marked, one at $\frac{3}{8}$" from the left side and the other $\frac{3}{8}$" from the handhold line, leaving the mortise width of $\frac{3}{8}$".

PROFILING THE SOLE   The classical procedure is to cut the wedge mortise and throat, then profile the sole using a "mother" plane. The hollow is cut first, using a round molding plane of the proper curvature fitted with a fence. According to Armour's magazine series (Roberts 1983), the round is then profiled using this hollow plane. I prefer to profile the sole at this point, along with other changes which strike me as less subject to mistake for an inexperienced maker.

You have a number of possible ways to shape your hollow plane's sole. If you choose the classical method, practice on a piece of scrap wood is strongly recommended. Using a table saw, the hollow profile may be roughed out by nibbling; using repeated passes over the sawblade with careful height adjustment between passes to just miss the scribed profile. I prefer to rough out the hollow with a cove cut on the table saw. If you are not familiar with this procedure, detailed instructions and safety precautions are available (Klausz 1993) or in most home workshop texts. A simple treatment is given at the end of this chapter. This method does not give a true circular arc (it is roughly elliptical), but the deviation is very slight, easily corrected in the next step.

In either table saw procedure, the hollow is trued and smoothed by using a scraper filed to the template

57

shape, mounted in a scratch stock similar to the one shown in Fig. 14.4.

The round is roughed out with either a hollow plane or a fore plane, approaching the scribed profile. It is finished as was the hollow, using a hollow scraper in a scratch stock. In both planes, care must be taken that the sole is straight front-to-back. If any point on the sole keeps the front of the mouth from contacting the work, the plane will behave very unsatisfactorily.

The bevel on the lower left side of the sole is cut, using a table saw (or planed away, if you prefer). The rabbet for the handhold is cut in the right top of the stock along the layout lines, using the table saw (saving the piece removed to make the wedge).

CUTTING THE THROAT The professional used two cuts of a backsaw to start the throat. For inexperienced hands, the table saw, carefully set and with the blade truly vertical, is more likely to produce an accurate result.

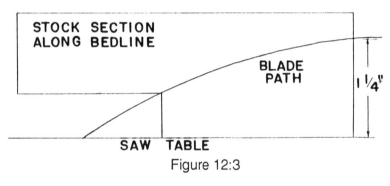

Figure 12:3

The mouth and the lower part of the throat are begun by two careful cuts with this tool. A section view of the saw set-up is seen in Fig. 12:3. The blade height is adjusted to just over $1\frac{1}{4}$" (a height gauge is almost a necessity here). The miter gauge is set to 40° (the complement of the pitch angle), using a protractor rather than the scale on the miter gauge (unless you have great confidence in it). The cut must be stopped at the point where the blade just starts to cut into the handhold. A stop is placed on the table saw surface to prevent cutting too far. It is safest to clamp the stock to the miter gauge for this operation, to avoid the drift which is a hazard in miter cuts. It is

clamped in a position that starts the cut between the bed and mouth lines you have marked on the sole, just removing the bed line. The flatness of the bed, an important factor in the performance of the plane, rests on this cut. In your first attempt, it is not being overly cautious to spend the better part of an hour making sure that the set-up is correct and making a trial run on scrap wood before cutting.

The second cut, starting the front of the throat, is made with the miter gauge set at 30°. Reset the stop marking the end of the cut, again positioning it to stop just as the blade reaches the handhold. Cut behind the mouth line, just removing it.

The waste wood between these cuts is now removed, using a thin chisel (you may choose to use careful nibbling cuts on the table saw to begin the process). The left wall of the throat is to be formed at a uniform distance of $\frac{3}{8}$" from the left side of the stock. The initial saw cuts are deepened with a chisel, stopping a quarter of an inch below the step of the handhold, and the throat is cleared of waste wood. Do not overcut; stop short of the final surface to allow for finishing (preferably with the floats to be described below).

The wedge mortise is now to be sunk from the top of the stock, to meet the lower throat just formed. This is begun by drilling a hole from the top of the stock. A professional would have bored from the top with a hand brace, but a drill press is safer for us. Begin by outlining the mortise on top of the stock along its layout lines with a sharp chisel, and remove a wedge of wood to permit the drill to start on a horizontal surface. A simple jig (described at the end of the chapter) is made to support the stock at the proper angle (40° from the press table) and in a true vertical plane. With these aids, a drill bit equal in diameter to the final width of the mortise may be used. If you are not confident in the ability of your equipment to drill accurately, it is safer to use a smaller drill. However, the sides of holes drilled to the finished dimension provide useful guidance for the paring operations. All of the mortises described in this book were started in this manner, and I have had no reason to regret this. Start the drill with a center punch mark centered in the mortise outline and placed to have the drill hole tangent to the bedline. Drill through into the lower throat, with care to avoid splintering on exit. (If you prefer to avoid power tools, use a smaller bit or rely entirely on chisels.)

The mortise may now be completed by sawing and chiselling. A planemaker's saw (sometimes called a saw float) was the tool of choice. These are now only rarely available (through antique tool dealers). They can be made, but a reasonable substitute is available in the Japanese keyhole saw stocked by fine tool dealers. This has a narrow blade that cuts on the pull stroke. It may be started in the hole just drilled, and used to remove the bulk of the waste from the mortise. Do not try to saw to the final outline, just clear the way to permit finishing with paring chisels and floats.

Finishing the throat is a procedure in which we have no assistance from modern tools. Sharp paring chisels (a pair of skew chisels is useful) can complete the task, but if you plan to make more than one or two planes, time will be saved if you make (or otherwise acquire) the floats described below. This step is one of the crucial determinants of your tool's performance.

The final throat should have a bed that provides a plane surface to support the back of the cutting iron. It is permissible to have small areas slightly below bed level, but no high points which prevent firm support of the iron just above its cutting edge are to be tolerated. (Some old molding planes have beds deliberately hollowed slightly to maximize wedge pressure at top and bottom of the iron.) The front of the throat should also be made flat, to support the front of the wedge.

THE IRONS Molding plane irons may be obtained from antique tool dealers, and you may be able to find a pair which can be adapted to your tools. Unfortunately, a large proportion of old irons have not been treated kindly over the years, and most have suffered some corrosion. Surface rust is acceptable if there is no pitting. Any pits in the front of the iron (opposite the bevel) near the cutting edge will require lapping away this surface to the depth of the deepest pit, if a satisfactory edge is to be won. Old irons were made by welding a strip of steel to wrought iron bodies. The line of demarkation of the steel to iron weld is usually visible. Be sure that the steel has not been depleted by extensive sharpening.

It is not impossible to sharpen an old iron and profile the sole of the stock to match it; this was done with the astragal plane of Chapter 13. It is easier to profile the sole and grind the iron to fit, with either an old iron or one newly made.

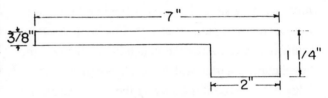

Figure 12:4

Irons were made for these two planes from O-1 tool steel, using the following procedure. They are hacksawn from $\frac{1}{8}$" stock, the lower sections $1\frac{1}{4}$" wide and the tangs a bit less than $\frac{3}{8}$" wide (see Fig. 12:4). Two inches is more than enough for the length of the lower section, and overall length of seven inches is enough.

The older irons have a slight taper, thinner at the top of the tang. This is of some help in releasing a tight wedge setting, but is not essential. I prefer to cut my tangs slightly short, and cold work the iron with a cross peen hammer on an anvil (a length of railroad track serves well), striking with the peen across the length to draw out the length and provide a slight taper. This process is finished with a planishing hammer and files or a belt sander. Hardening and tempering are described in Chapter 23.

WEDGE With the blank iron available (either an old one or one of your make), the wedge may be fitted. The strip of wood removed from the handhold is planed to a uniform thickness equal to the width of the mortise ($\frac{3}{8}$", unless it grew somewhat during cutting). It is cut into the wedge shape of slightly more than 10° (the difference between the 50° bed and the 60° mortise front, plus the iron taper angle). The interior of the wedge mortise will probably have to be refined with a side float (or a file) to permit entry of the wedge. The iron is inserted in the throat, and the fit of the wedge checked. The taper is adjusted by planing to create a tight fit along its full length, tightest at the bottom.

IRON PROFILE With the iron blank wedged in place, its rear is scribed to match exactly the sole profile. It is helpful to coat the back of the iron with machinist's layout dye first, to make the scribe line more easily visible. The iron is filed and ground to this scribe line, initially at right angles to the face, without a bevel. After the match is satisfactory, the bevel may be started with a file. Do not file to a sharp edge (which would not survive the crude hardening process described here), but leave the cutting edge blunt.

If you have not hardened steel before, you may prefer to find a blacksmith or a machine tool firm who will do this for you. For irons larger than the present pair, this would be the wiser course, unless you have a forge or a welding torch. In the present case, doing it yourself adds another dimension to your participation in an old art. The procedure is detailed in Chapter 23, tempering to a deep straw color at the cutting edge.

FITTING The tempered blade may now have the bevel completed, to produce the cutting edge. A grinder serves initially, but unless you have mastered the technique of grinding to a thin edge without softening the steel, it is safer to grind only to the point where there is a small flat at the profile. (A blue color can develop quickly at the edge, and if it does, rehardening will be needed.)

The temper was chosen to permit developing the final bevel with a file, and this is now done. (A water-cooled, slow speed grinding wheel may also be used.) As the cutting edge is developed, it is

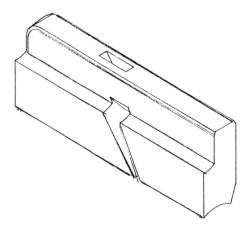

Figure 12:5

constantly monitored by positioning the iron in the stock and sighting along the sole. If any section is cut too far back, the entire edge must be reduced to this level and this is more tedious than frequent checking. The process is complete only when the entire edge is sharp, and the iron may be positioned in the stock to expose a uniform hairline of cutting edge over the entire profile. Be prepared to spend a great deal of time to accomplish this. Until it is achieved, your tool will cut roughly.

FINISHING Your plane is now a working tool, but a number of finishing touches are required. The upper side of the side escapement, where the wedge peeks from its mortise, is tapered with a chisel to prevent any shavings hangup there. This is seen in the sketch of the finished stock of the hollow in Fig. 12:5. The lower edge of the wedge is truncated a short distance above the cutting edge of the iron, and is tapered on the exposed side to guide shavings toward the exit (Fig. 12:6). The wedge finial is shaped to a profile that pleases you (I chose the circular finial used in most early eighteenth century molders). The

Figure 12:6

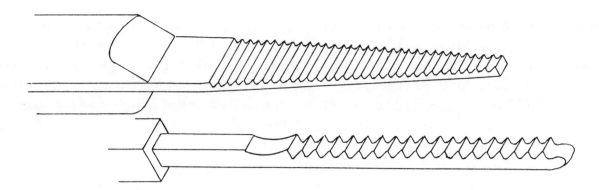

Figure 12:7

step of the handhold is molded, a round plane being called into service for the planes pictured; but shaped as you please. The upper rear corner of the stock is rounded to provide a comfortable grip for your right hand. The upper arrises are rounded or chamfered with a plane, to ease the left hand's task. This treatment is continued down the upper sides of the stock, using a freshly honed chisel. The vertical chamfers are terminated at the step and at the same height on the left side by cuts of a $\frac{1}{8}$" gouge (a rat-tail file might serve). All surfaces are smoothed with scraper or sandpaper.

The classical finish is achieved by soaking in linseed oil. Rubbing in boiled linseed oil, wiping off after an hour or so, and drying for a day or more - followed by several repetitions - produces a reasonable facsimile of the appearance of the planes as they used to be made.

FLOATS   Two planemaker's floats are sketched in Fig. 12:7, one made in my shop and the other a gift from a fellow planemaker. Although these are not essential for making a molding plane, they so greatly assist that they are worth making if you plan to make more than one tool. (They may be found, rarely, at antique tool auctions, but are usually in poor shape, expensive, and require reconditioning and resharpening with almost as much effort as starting fresh.) They may be described as very coarse files, but in fact provide a series of scraping edges that can remove wood rapidly yet leave a smooth surface. (Until you have them, make do with an assortment of files and sanding sticks.)

The topping float starts as a piece of soft steel of rectangular section, about $\frac{1}{4}$" square. The side float is made from steel $\frac{1}{8}$" thick and $\frac{3}{4}$" wide, cut to taper to a width of about $\frac{1}{4}$" at the lower end. A series of cuts is made in one surface with a triangular file, to form an outline like the teeth of a rip saw. This can be done free-hand, but a better result is obtained by making a simple jig to guide the file and provide for moving the workpiece a uniform distance (about $\frac{1}{8}$") as each cut is completed. Coating the work surface with machinist's layout dye, and stopping each cut just as the last trace of dye is removed from the tip of the previous tooth, speeds the task (Kahn, 1994). The tools work very satisfactorily without hardening, even if made from dead soft steel. They will serve for a number of planes before they need resharpening.

(An alternate style of making floats is given by Sperling and Chapin, 1981.)

JIG   The simple jig for holding the stock in position for drilling the wedge mortise was made from two pieces of plywood with battens attached at the proper angle to support bottom and toe of the stock (one of these is shown in Fig. 12:8). The two pieces are clamped together

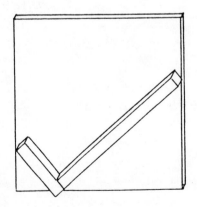

Figure 12:8

61

with the stock between them, and the assembly is checked with a square against the drill press table to make sure the stock is held vertically.

COVE CUTS Coves may be cut on a table saw by guiding the workpiece over the saw blade at an angle, using a diagonal fence clamped to the saw table on the operator's side of the blade. The position is sketched in Fig.12:9. The location of this fence is determined as follows:

The hollow arc to be developed is drawn on the sole of the workpiece. Set the sawblade height to reach to the highest point of this arc. Make a template of two strips of wood tacked to crosspieces which hold them parallel, separated by a distance equal to the width spanned by the arc at the bottom of the workpiece. A cardboard template will also serve, and this is shown in Fig. 12:10 for clarity. (The black arc represents the sawblade.) Place the template to strad-

dle the blade, and tilt it until it touches the teeth at both ends of the exposed blade, as shown in the figure. This determines the angle at which to mount the temporary fence. It is clamped to the table, at a distance from the leading edge of the sawblade equal to the distance of the start of the arc from the left side of the work.

With the temporary fence securely clamped to the saw table, lower the blade until only $\frac{1}{32}$" or so is exposed. Guiding the workpiece by this fence, pass it over the spinning blade. Make repeated passes, increasing the sawblade elevation very slightly after each pass. Compare the progress of the cuts with the scribed arc on the work after each pass, and make slight adjustments in the fence position if necessary. Continue until the cove matches the scribed arc. This operation is one of the most hazardous on the table saw, and should be approached with caution.

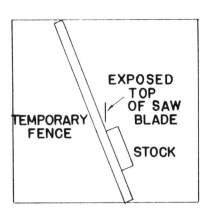

Figure 12:9

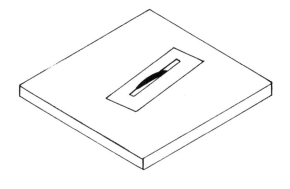

Figure 12:10

CHAPTER 13

ASTRAGAL MOLDING PLANE
Making a plane to fit a molding iron

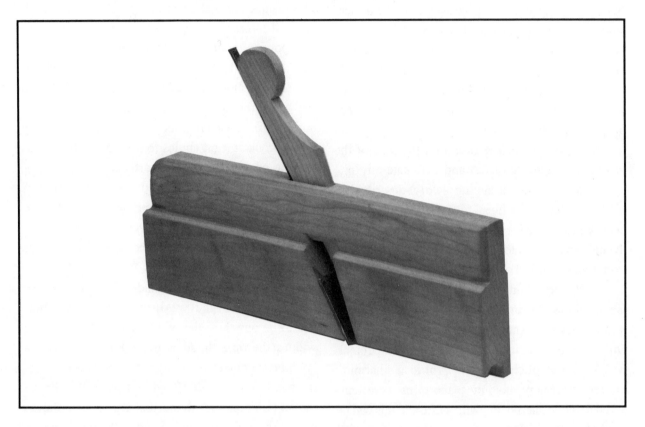

This plane was made following the classical sequence outlined by W.J. Armour in 1898, in which the throat is formed before molding the sole (in contrast to the one described for most other molders covered in this book). It departed from the classical method in that an existing iron was to be used. The plane's sole profile was matched to the iron, rather than filing the iron to match the sole. A beginning planemaker would be well advised to avoid this sequence for any iron profile except the simplest. However, it did produce a useable tool, and is offered here as an alternate for your consideration.

An authentic molding plane iron may be found occasionally at antique tool dealers or tool auctions. Select one that has a profile that interests you, with no significant pitting on its face (else it will not repay

sharpening). The iron used in this case is from an astragal plane, which cuts a convex semicircular profile flanked by two short horizontal surfaces (fillets). The common astragal has both a fence (to guide the cut along the edge of the work) and a depth stop (to ensure that the cut reaches a uniform depth over its length). Both features are integral to the stock, similar to those seen in Fig. 12:1.

The present plane omits the depth stop. This permits it to be used in making compound profiles, where the astragal is cut outboard of another molding which would stop the astragal cut before it was complete. Provision should be made to control the depth of cut in such use. If you prefer to incorporate a conventional depth stop in your plane, use a stock $\frac{1}{4}$" wider and rabbet the lower portion of this extra width to create one, its height just over the deepest cut of the sole profile. All other directions are unchanged, except as noted.

THE IRON   The $\frac{3}{4}$" iron used here was from a collection of old irons bought at an antique tool auction. (If your iron is of a different width, the dimensions given in the procedure below must of course be altered accordingly.) Because it cuts a full semicircle, the plane it fits is designed to be held vertically in use. Most other profiles call for mounting in a plane which is used at an angle, or "sprung", as in the ogee of the next chapter.

Remove any surface rust from the face of the blade (the unbeveled side) and eliminate any pits with a coarse stone or a lapping plate (as described on p.14), finishing with finer stones. If any pits remain near the cutting edge, they will leave their mark on the molding the plane cuts. (The old saying was "the iron writes its name on the work".) The cutting edge is then sharpened on the bevel side with slip stones (small stones of teardrop section in various sizes). If it is in very poor shape, the process may be begun with a small stone in a hand tool such as a Dremel, with some risk of changing the profile and harming the temper. Many molding plane irons were tempered to allow sharpening with a file, and this can be tried. The final edge should be sharp over its full length.

LAYOUT   A block of wood (I used hard maple) is squared to $9\frac{1}{2}$ x $3\frac{3}{8}$ x 1", having considered the requirements spelled out in Chapter 1. Layout lines are sketched in Fig. 13:1. The bed line (the line of intersection of the back of the throat with the sole) is scribed across the sole at right angles to the sides, at a distance of $3\frac{1}{2}$" from the toe. A second line is marked across the sole, $\frac{3}{16}$" nearer the toe; this is the (temporary) mouth line. Both sides of the stock are marked with the bed angle, starting at the bed line and slanting upward away from the toe at 60° ("cabinet" pitch for hardwood; it would be 50° for use on soft wood). These are joined by a line across the top of the stock at right angles to the sides. This marks the rear edge of the wedge mortise.

A line for the front of the wedge mortise is scribed across the top, 1" nearer the toe than the previous one. This is joined to the mouth line by scribing the breast line on each side of the stock, for guidance in cutting the mortise.

A portion of the top right side of the stock is to be marked for removal. It was usual for the wedge mortise to be one-third the width of the handhold (the width at the top of the stock after rabbeting). To use a $\frac{1}{4}$" mortise chisel for cutting the wedge mortise, the handhold is made $\frac{3}{4}$" wide, leaving $\frac{1}{4}$" for the rabbet (a bit smaller than usual unless you plan to include a depth stop, which makes the rabbet width $\frac{1}{2}$"). Layout lines for the rabbet are drawn on top of

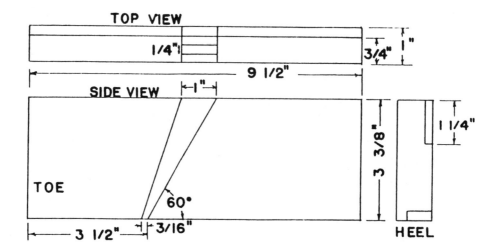

Figure 13:1

the stock at ¾" from the left side, and at 1¼" from the top on the right side. Lines marking the sides of the wedge mortise are scribed on top of the stock, at ¼" and ½" from the left side.

STOCK The handhold is formed by sawing away the rabbet on the right side of the stock along the layout lines. The horizontal step is coved with a small round plane.

The throat is begun by sawing along the diagonal layout lines on the right side of the stock. The saw cut determines the accuracy of the bedding of the plane, and must be done with care. The cut must be perpendicular to the side, reach a depth of ¾" at the sole of the plane but only cut ¼" deep in the stock at a point just above the coved step (as shown in Fig. 13:2. These dimensions are increased by ¼" if you allowed for a depth stop.) The old planemakers would do this with a backsaw. If you choose to hand saw, a good miter box is recommended unless you are better than I am at handling a saw. Using a table saw, the blade height is set at ¾", the miter gauge set to 30°, and the stock clamped to the miter gauge to prevent creep. A mark on the tablesaw top is made to indicate where the gauge has to be stopped to prevent cutting into the handhold, and the cut is made. The miter gauge set to cut along the breast line, the stock clamped, the stop reset, and the cut made. (A fuller description of this process is given on p.58).

The waste between these saw cuts is now removed with chisels. The saw cuts are deepened with chisels to the same level the cuts have at the sole, all the way to the level of the coved step. Use care to ensure that the surfaces established by the saw cuts are maintained and extended inward, where necessary, during this step. These become the bed for the iron and the bearing surface for the wedge, and must be made flat.

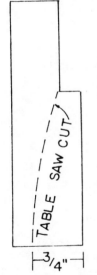

Figure 13:2

The wedge mortise may now be completed, cutting from the top of the stock, following the procedure outlined on pp.58-59. Care is required to avoid splintering the wood when breaking through into the lower section. Scribing the mortise outline from below with a sharp chisel is recommended.

Planemaker's floats (see p.61) are of great value in finishing this operation. In their absence, a four-square file will do the job, although much more slowly. With the wedge mortise completed to your satisfaction, the material between bed and breast and above the coved step is pared away to taper into the side opening, just enough to prevent shavings hangup (as shown in Figure 12:5).

A rabbet may now be cut at the bottom of the body to form the fence. The fence thickness is 9/32", leaving a 1/32" recess in the fence for the left side of the cutting edge of the iron. The rabbet is sawn away, placing the new sole ¼" above the old one.

The right side of the cutting edge of the iron must extend very slightly beyond the right side of the sole. Should it be set improperly, the stock will not be able to enter the cut being made, and the plane will be forced outward as the cut progresses. The left side of the iron will be slightly inset into the fence, to avoid trapping shavings between fence and iron. Be sure to allow for proper lateral placement of the iron in laying out the sole profile.

WEDGE The wedge may now be made. In wider planes, the waste sawn away to form the handhold provides the material for this, but in the present case another source is found. A piece 8" x 1" is planed to the thickness accommodated by the wedge mortise (¼"), and cut diagonally at one end at the angle between the diagonal lines scribed on the plane body in the initial layout. The iron and wedge are inserted into their mortise, and observed for fit. The front of the wedge is carefully planed until it contacts the front of the mortise over its full length, preferably fitting more tightly at its lower end. The extra length allowed in the blank used allows for repeated planing adjustments in attaining this fit. You may wish to use chalk to locate tight spots in the fit.

With the wedge fit to your satisfaction, the lower end is marked for cutting off at the lowest level which will not interfere with the shavings rising from the face of the iron. It is sawn off on a diagonal, the long end at the inside of the mortise, the cut terminating in a horizontal line when the wedge is in position as shown in Fig.12:6. The next step is shaping the sole.

SOLE The sole profile is not the same as the profile of the iron. The vertical dimensions must be decreased, because of the angle at which the iron is bedded. With the iron wedged in position, careful measurements are made of vertical heights of the principal features of its profile. These are transferred to the heel of the plane, and the required sole profile is scribed from them. Waste is nibbled away with a plow plane or a table saw, taking care to remain within the scribed outline.

A scraper is made by scribing the required profile on a sheet steel blank (a piece of saw blade or cabinet scraper blade may be used). This is carefully ground and/or filed to shape. The face and profiled edge are honed, keeping the profiled edge at right angles to the face. It is set in a beader such as a Stanley #66 or a wooden equivalent; I used the one sketched in Fig.14:4. Careful use of this finishes the roughed out sole profile. It is important that the sole be straight toe-to-heel, which is ensured by keeping the fence of the beader tightly against the side of the stock. Stop frequently to wedge the iron in place and assess the match with the sole profile. Refine the scraper profile as necessary. The task is time consuming, and is finished only when the sole permits the iron to be set showing a uniform, slender line of steel (the thickness of a fine shaving) protruding from the sole profile. As this point is approached, trial cuts made on scrap stock with the plane help to point out required adjustments.

You may consider making slight changes in the iron profile if the match between sole and iron proves elusive. Do not be in too much haste to do this; the grass may not be much greener on that side of the fence. Jumping back and forth between changing the sole and the iron is ineffective.

Your task is not complete until the iron may be set to show a uniform cutting edge exposure over the full profile, and it cuts a satisfactory molding.

FINISHING With the plane performing well, you are ready for the finishing touches. The stock is cleaned by polish planing, scraping and/or sanding. The top of the wedge is marked with a finial outline that pleases you, cut to shape, and sanded. The stock is rounded at top rear to provide a comfortable grip, and the top arrises are softened (here chamfered at 45° with a plane). These are met with matching vertical chamfers cut with a freshly sharpened chisel, and terminated by gouge cuts. The heel view of the finished stock is seen in Fig. 13:3. After a final trial cut to enjoy your new tool, a coating of your choice is applied. I used boiled linseed oil thinned 1:1 with turpentine and well rubbed in, followed after drying with another coat of straight linseed.

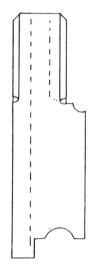

Figure 13:3

66

CHAPTER 14

GRECIAN OGEE
A boxed and sprung molding plane

In this chapter are introduced two new features, found in many molding planes. The first is a stock designed to be held at an angle (the spring angle) when in use. The reason for this lies in the fact that the plane's throat expands (at the wedge angle) as it approaches its top. The higher a segment of the cutting edge is located in the throat, the wider is the mouth in front of it. To keep the mouth opening as small and uniform as possible, the profile is positioned to keep it within the smallest possible vertical span; which most often means at an angle. The stock of the plane must be held at this spring angle while it is in use, to cut the molding desired. This provides a second advantage. Using the plane at this angle, your hand pressure tends to keep the fence firmly against the guiding edge of the workpiece.

The second new feature is the use of boxing to improve wear characteristics. Molding profiles that contain quirks (narrow indentations) require their molding planes to have sharp projecting ridges on their soles (one is seen in Fig. 12:1). If these are formed in the beechwood of the plane stock, they are subject to rapid wear. The beech of these sole portions, in the better grade of plane, is replaced with boxwood to provide better wear characteristics. A strip of boxwood about $\frac{1}{8}$" thick is glued into a slot in the sole, at the location where the quirk is to be formed. Beech and boxwood are shaped simultaneously as the sole profile is generated.

While the term "boxing" is applied universally, it is not unknown to use another wood, such as lignum vitae, for the inserted slips. The boxing described here, "slip" boxing, is not the only type found. The more difficult task of dovetailing larger pieces of boxwood into the stock to protect wear areas will not be covered, but a description may be found in Whelan (1993).

Boxing slips may be cut with their grain direction parallel to that of the stock. In this case, the thin boxwood projection is subject to breakage along the grain. Another consideration is that better wear would be obtained if the end grain of the boxwood were used on the wear surface. For these two reasons, a vertical grain orientation of the boxing slip would be best. However, this would leave one section of the boxing slip — the one which supports the quirk area of the cutting iron — at risk of breaking off along its short grain. To avoid this, the best grade of molding plane has boxing slips cut with the grain running diagonally downward from heel to toe, at the bed angle. (The grain direction is shown in Fig. 14:1.) This is the optimum compromise between wear resistance and resistance to breakage at the mouth.

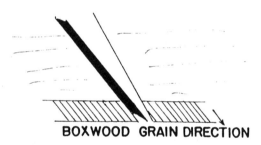

BOXWOOD GRAIN DIRECTION

Figure 14:1

As this orientation of the boxwood grain requires slices diagonally across the long dimension of the boxwood log, it is rather impractical for today's planemaker to waste boxwood by cutting the slips full length in this orientation. He resorts to joining shorter pieces. Examination of older boxed molding planes frequently shows diagonal gaps in their boxing, too. It is difficult to ascertain whether the slips were pieced initially, or they were originally full-length and split through shrinkage over the years (but I suspect the former is true).

As we have seen in the earlier chapters on the bench planes, it is preferable for the grain of their stocks to run downward from toe to heel, the orientation that best resists splintering by the workpiece. Planes for cutting architectural moldings, however, are used on wood of very straight grain without defect (the moldings would not be very good otherwise) and the grain direction of their soles is not particularly important — unless they are boxed, as we shall see.

Professional planemakers used "mother" or "backing" planes to cut the soles of their "daughter" planes. The mother and daughter planes have profiles that fit together like hand in glove, touching at every point. In making a mother plane for a given profile, a choice must be made; should the mother be designed to cut from toe to heel of the daughter, or in the completely different design that cuts from heel to toe. Mother planes intended to cut unboxed molders may be found in either configuration. The planemaker presumably chose to orient the grain of his plane blank for easiest planing in the direction required by his mother plane. Examination of the grain orientation of early unboxed molders indicates a slight preference for the same direction as used in the bench planes; grain sloping down from toe to heel. The opposite direction, however, is often seen.

Mother planes used to cut boxed profiles, on the other hand, would be expected to be configured to cut from heel to toe of the daughter plane, the direction demanded by the boxing. All of such mother planes I have examined are designed to do so. Examination of the grain direction of the older boxed molding planes indicates that the grain of the beech was chosen to favor this direction of planing, the grain running down from heel to toe. This is not always true of later boxed molding planes made by large makers, who used "stickers", machine driven rotary cutters, to form the profiles. The speed of such cutting edges makes them less sensitive to grain direction.

The point of this discussion is that if you plan to cut the sole profile of a boxed plane with hollow and round or other planes, choose for the heel of your stock the end from which the grain runs downward

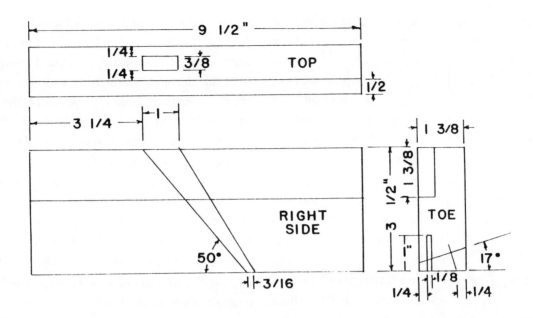

Figure 14:2

toward the sole (in contrast to the direction favored in unboxed planes).

BOXING The applewood plane of the photograph started as a squared block 9½ x 3½ x 1⅜". All of the dimensions given below and seen in Fig. 14:2 refer to this plane, and will need modification to meet your needs. Measuring them from a prototype you wish to duplicate is by far the wisest course, using the description below only to suggest sequence.

Cut a groove the full length of the sole for the boxwood, one inch deep, its outer edge ¼" from the right side of the sole. The old planemakers would use a narrow iron in a plow plane for this, but a table circular saw is more practical today. A standard carbide tipped blade gives a kerf of about the right width (⅛"). Using a thin kerf blade, more than one pass will be needed — be sure that these are parallel.

Cut slices of boxwood to a thickness of just over the width of your groove. These are carefully planed to remove the saw marks and finish with uniform thickness, fitting snugly into the groove in the sole. A close fit is required for a strong glue joint; remember that the rear section of boxing slip supports a part of the blade and must withstand part of the thrust upon it. Having attained this fit, slips are cut to a

height of one inch, preferably on a diagonal to have the grain orientation seen in Fig. 14:1. These are cut and trimmed to fit together as an assembly which will fill the length of the groove. The boxwood slips are glued in place, butting the pieces together tightly; yellow carpenter's glue is satisfactory.

SOLE PROFILE The sole profile you wish to create is to be scribed on the toe of the plane. A spring angle is chosen to make the molding profile lie as nearly horizontal as possible (17° in the plane illustrated). The vertical spring mark is scribed on the toe, at this angle with the side of the stock, starting ¼" from the left side of the sole (which is on your right as you mark the toe). This marks the inner side of the fence of the plane. Sketch the outline of the profile you wish your plane to cut, placing the end which will be nearest to the edge of the ultimate workpiece at the fence. This profile is laid out on the toe, beginning from the vertical spring mark and with its other end an eighth of an inch or so above the bottom of the block. The quirk, of course, is placed on the boxing slip. The horizontal spring mark is scribed just above the highest point of the profile, at right angles to the vertical spring mark. These marks may

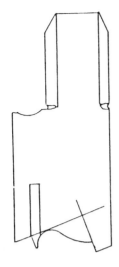

Figure 14:3

be seen in the toe view of the finished plane in Fig.14:3.

Lacking a mother plane, an accomplished woodworker can rough out the molding profile with a plow plus hollows and rounds. I prefer the safer course of cutting the portion next to the boxing with a round-nose bit in a power router (cutting beech and boxwood simultaneously), and roughing out the rest of the profile by careful nibbling with the table saw.

The sole is finished with a scraping tool called a scratch stock. The profile originally marked on the stock is cut in thin steel (a section of a scraper or saw blade serves) with files or a hand grinder. Face and profile are honed, the profiled edge at right angles to the face. This scraper blade is mounted in a simple holder shaped to provide a fence and a slot for the scraper, as shown in Fig. 14:4. Be sure that the blade is held tightly in this tool, and will not move during use. The scratch stock may be worked in either direction, blade kept vertical, to refine the rough sole profile. Be sure to keep the front-to-back lines of the sole dead straight, by keeping the scratch stock fence firmly against the side of the stock. Continue until no more scrapings are removed.

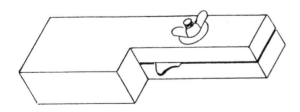

Figure 14:4

With the tilt of the table saw blade set at the spring angle, the bottom of the fence (the lower left side of the stock, below the profile) is beveled along the spring mark. With the stock on its right side and the blade at the same angle, a cut is made on the bottom side of the (nearly) horizontal spring mark, just deep enough to reach the boxing. The right side of the boxing is cut away to be parallel to the vertical spring mark. (The cuts of this paragraph may be made with a shoulder plane, if you prefer.) The finished profile of the toe is seen in Fig.14:3.

Most U.S.catalogs show outlines for their molding planes with quirks having fairly wide flat sections at the bottom. Such wide flats are not often seen in actual planes. Wide molders may be found with quirks having flats as wide as $\frac{1}{8}$", but most quirks observed have narrow flat bottoms, or bottoms rounded as shown in Fig.14:3.

THROAT LAYOUT As shown in Fig. 14:2, the bedline on the top of the stock is drawn at $3\frac{1}{4}$" from the heel, and the line for the front of the wedge mortise is placed one inch forward of this. The left side of the wedge mortise is marked at $\frac{1}{4}$" from the side, directly over the fence at the sole. The right side is marked $\frac{3}{8}$" further in. (This makes the wedge a bit thicker than the classic 1:1:1 ratio on the top.) The edge of the handhold rabbet is marked a further $\frac{1}{4}$" in, or $\frac{1}{2}$" from the right side, and a line on the right side $1\frac{3}{8}$" down from the top marks the level of the step. Bedlines are marked on both sides from the ends of the top bedline, down and forward at 50°. The lines marking the throat front are drawn on the sides, from the end of the front wedge mortise line on top to a point $\frac{3}{16}$" in front of the side bedline at the level of the depth stop.

THROAT The formation of throat and wedge has been covered in detail in the two previous chapters, so that a brief description should serve here. The bed and throat fronts are begun by sawcuts as described on p.58. The left side of the lower throat is cut deep enough to slightly indent the fence. The wedge mortise is begun by drilling in a press, using a $\frac{3}{8}$" bit and a jig similar to that shown in Fig.12:8 and described on p.61. Continue with a sharp $\frac{3}{8}$"

mortise chisel. Care is required to avoid marring the profiled sole edges in this step; the stock may be held by its sides in a vise, using soft wood padding to protect it. Finish with paring chisels and floats (or a 4-square file). Rabbet for the handhold along its layout lines. The step of the handhold is molded, a hollow plane serving in the present instance. Taper the area above the handhold into the escapement, in the same manner as described for the plane of Fig. 12:5. The wedge blank is made from the handhold waste, and shaping begun as described on p.59.

IRON   The iron is made from $3/32$ x 1" ground flat stock, annealed tool steel. Leave $2\frac{1}{2}$" at full width, and hacksaw away all but $\frac{1}{4}$" of the width for a distance equal to the length of the tang. If you plan to taper this, it is cut out $\frac{1}{4}$" wide by five inches long and cold worked with a cross-peen hammer on an anvil as described in Chapter 12 — or the tang may be left at original thickness, if cut to a six inch length. Alternatively, acquire an old iron with an unpitted face and with enough steel left to take the desired profile shape.

The wedge may now be fitted with the iron blank in place. As always, it must grip the lower part of the blade firmly. Wedge the iron into position, with the wide section just short of the upper limit of its travel. The sole outline is carefully scribed on its back (machinist's lay-out dye makes this easier). The profile is roughed out with a bench grinder, and refined with files and hand grinder. Cut the profile without a bevel; that is, cut at right angles to the blade surface. This reproduces the desired profile on the front of the blade, where it is needed. The bevel may now be started on the rear of the iron with files. Do not complete the bevel at this stage, as a sharp edge will not survive the hardening operation; leave the edge dull.

The process of hardening the blade is given in Chapter 23. Briefly, the wide section of the blade is heated to full red, and quenched in water. Check with a file to be sure the hardening has been effected; the file should not cut. Polish the wide section of the blade, and heat the area furthest from the cutting edge. As the temper colors develop, a straw color is noted in the hottest area and moves toward the cutting edge, followed by a blue. When the deep straw reaches the edge, quench at once in water. This temper is a compromise; hard enough to hold an edge, soft enough to permit shaping with a file. The heat treatment is, of course, unnecessary if you are using an old iron.

The sharpening may now be completed with files and slip stones, with frequent examination of the match of the cutting edge to the sole profile. Continue until all sections of the profile are razor sharp, and show a uniform thin exposure above the plane's sole. The ultimate test of this fitting, of course, is the ability to cut a smooth molding.

FINISHING   The wedge is tapered at its bottom to avoid interference with shavings (as in Fig.12:6), and its finial shaped to please you. The rear top of the stock is rounded for a comfortable grip, the top arrises chamfered ($5/16$"wide at 60° is shown) and the chamfers continued down toe and heel to terminate in gouge cuts at the step level. Polish plane and scrape, and apply a finish (two coats of tung oil for the plane shown).

CHAPTER 15

DADO PLANE

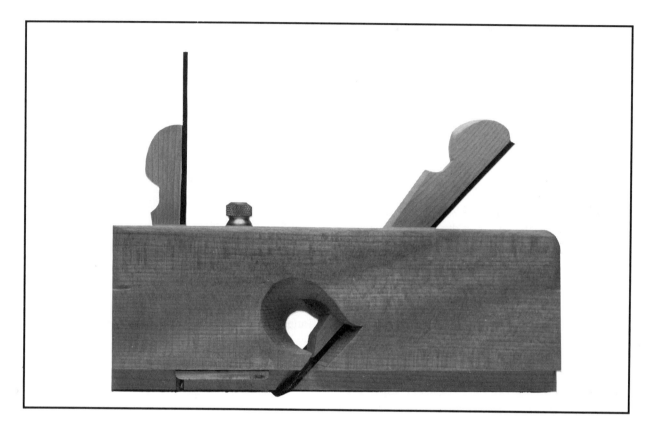

The name "dado" has had a checkered history. In classical architecture, it referred to the middle, flat section of the pedestal of a column. When it became popular to use a protective, ornamental paneling on the lower parts of interior walls, the name was borrowed to describe this. In one form of wall treatment, the lower edge of the panel frame was inset into a groove in the floorboards. This groove was given the same name. The name "dado" was generalized to mean any related groove. And when a plane was developed to cut them, it, too, assumed the name.

Many furniture pieces call for a groove to be made in a direction across the grain of the wood. Today these would be made with a power router or a dado head in a table saw. (In some cases, the cut can be finished with a dado plane in less time than it takes to set up a machine.) Examples are the slots inside a chest of drawers to take the drawer runners, or in the

sides of a bookshelf to allow the shelves to be housed. If a simple rabbet plane were used for this, it would splinter the wood along the sides of its cut because its blade peels, rather than cuts, the lengthwise wood fibers crossing its path. Before the dado plane was developed in the mid-eighteenth century, it was necessary to first saw, or at least score with a knife, along the lines marking the edges of the groove. The dado accomplishes this latter task and finishes the groove in one operation. It is equipped with a nicker or scribing iron which severs the wood fibers along the sides of the cut before the main iron reaches them.

Three new operations are introduced in this chapter: the rabbet type throat, a mortise for a skewed wedge, and fitting a depth stop. These provide rather more difficulty than the steps required in planes treated up to this point, and make the dado a poor choice for a first attempt at planemaking. As with the hollow and round, there is little reason to make this plane simply to acquire one. Old ones are readily available at no great cost, at tool meets or from antique tool dealers. Making one, however, will convince you that a high level of skill is required to match the products of the early planemakers.

Even more than the planes covered earlier, using a professionally made dado as a prototype is highly desirable. The skew angle provides many opportunities for error in laying out the cuts, and constant reference to the model helps to avoid these. An even better reason is to admire its workmanship after you struggle with the skew mortise. My prototype was a $\frac{7}{8}$" dado by John Denison (ca.1840-76).

IRONS An old iron was found which approximately matched the one in the prototype. Its cutting edge slanted across the width at an angle of 80°, and was $\frac{7}{8}$" wide. In order to ensure the absence of surface defects, the face (unbeveled side) was flattened on a lapping plate and water stones. The nicker iron was a bit more trouble. A spare molding plane iron was reground to match the nicker of the prototype, leaving two knife-like projections (as seen in Fig. 15:1) positioned in front of the ends of the main iron's cutting edge. (Failing to find suitable irons, you can make them as detailed in Chapter 23.)

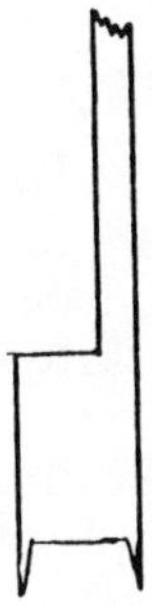

Figure 15:1

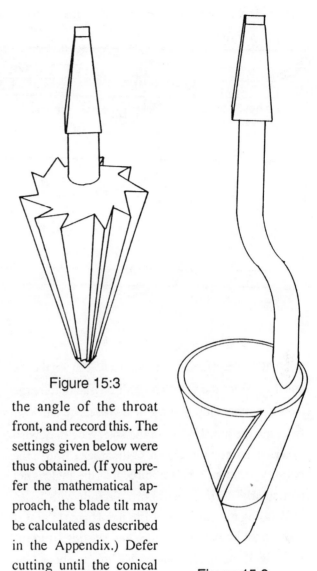

Figure 15:3

Figure 15:2

OVERVIEW, THROAT The sawcuts defining the lower throat front and the lower bedline are easily made on the table saw. You may determine the proper settings to use from your prototype in the following way. Place it sole down on the table of the saw, against the miter gauge, and set this gauge to the skew angle measured on top of the stock (in the direction that will allow a straight path for the blade along the bed). Change the tilt angle of the saw blade until it parallels the bed of the prototype. Remember that the bedline angle measured on the side of the prototype will be smaller than the angle the saw blade makes with the table, because of the skew cut. Record the values, tilt the blade to match the angle of the throat front, and record this. The settings given below were thus obtained. (If you prefer the mathematical approach, the blade tilt may be calculated as described in the Appendix.) Defer cutting until the conical throat is formed.

The gracefully curved throat opening was begun, by the professional makers, with a conical reamer designed for the purpose (Fig. 15:2). A reasonable substitute is a pipe reamer (Fig. 15:3), available from large tool or plumbing supply stores; it tapers from $1\frac{1}{2}$" to $\frac{1}{8}$" in a bit under $2\frac{1}{2}$". It cuts the beechwood of the stock surprisingly well.

THROAT The procedure and dimensions given here (Fig. 15:4) describe the making of the beechwood plane of the photograph. The blank is squared to $9\frac{1}{2}$ x $3\frac{1}{2}$ x $1\frac{3}{8}$". The center of the pilot hole for the rabbet throat is located on the right side of the stock (having considered the proper grain

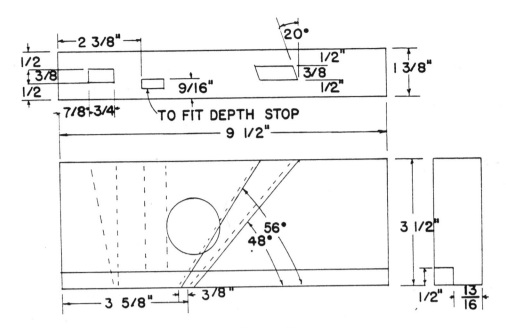

Figure 15:4

angle to 32° and decrease its exposure to 1¼", to just reach the conical hole on the right side. Leaving the miter gauge unchanged, make this cut just behind the mouth line. The angle with the sole, measured on the side of the stock, will be 56°. These cuts are shown in the second sketch of Fig. 15:5.

orientation described in Chapter 1), $4\frac{1}{8}$" from the toe and $1\frac{1}{4}$" from the sole. The drill bit should emerge from the other side of the stock with its center $3\frac{7}{8}$" from the toe and $1\frac{5}{8}$" from the sole. You may wish to scribe lines on top and toe of the stock to guide the boring operation. Sight this direction (the angle is not particularly critical), and bore through with a $\frac{5}{8}$" drill. Using the pipe reamer in a hand brace (a power drill might be hard to handle) and starting from the left side of the stock, enlarge this hole to about $1\frac{1}{2}$" diameter. If you are unable to find a suitable reamer, the conical hole could be cut with gouges and faired with files, but would require care and time to give comparable results. The top sketch of Fig. 15:5 shows the stock at this point.

Set the miter gauge of the table saw to 20°, the sawblade tilt angle at 40°. This will produce a bedline angle of about 48°. Set the blade exposure at $1\frac{7}{8}$", which will put the top of the cut about $1\frac{3}{8}$" above the bottom of the block. The bedline starts at $3\frac{5}{8}$" back of the toe on the right, angling back at 20° along the sole. The mouth line is $\frac{3}{8}$" forward of this and parallel to it. Clamp the stock to the miter gauge in position to have the blade pass just in front of the bedline, and make the cut. Decrease the saw blade tilt

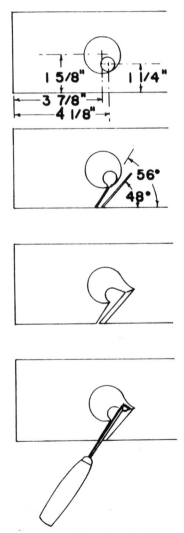

Figure 15:5

74

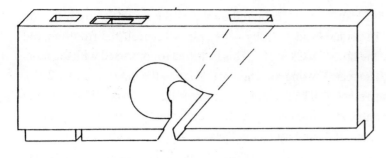

Figure 15:6

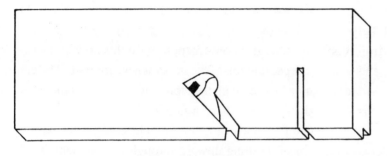

Figure 15:7

Mark bedlines on both sides of the stock, extending the bed cut, and join them on the top with the skew line marking the rear of the wedge mortise. A parallel line marking its front is placed $1\frac{1}{8}$" forward of this. Lines from the ends of this to the front of the mouth are drawn on each side, to guide the cutting of the mortise. The sides of the $\frac{3}{8}$" wide wedge mortise are scribed $\frac{1}{2}$" from each side, on top of the stock. Deepen these scribe marks with a chisel. Remove a wedge-shaped piece to provide a level area perpendicular to the bedline, to facilitate starting the drill.

A $\frac{3}{8}$" drill bit may be used if the stock is held on a drill press table with both its side and the bedline exactly vertical. (Use a jig similar to the one shown in Fig.12:8 to accomplish this. If the hole is to be drilled by hand, it is much safer to use a smaller drill.) The drill is started from a center punch mark in the level area, centered in its width and $\frac{1}{4}$" in front of the line marking the rear of the mortise. Stop the bit just short of breaking through into the conical hole, to avoid serious splintering. Square the upper part of the hole using a $\frac{3}{8}$" mortise chisel. (Both of these steps may be accomplished in one operation by use of a $\frac{3}{8}$" mortising attachment for the drill press, if one is available.)

Scribe an arc joining the circular opening on the left side of the stock to the top of the bedline saw cut. This converts the top of the throat opening into a graceful ogee as shown in Fig. 15:6. On the right side of the stock, scribe a tangent from the top of the circular opening to the top of the bedline cut, as seen in Fig. 15:7. With a turning saw or a coping saw, make a cut joining these two lines to rough out the top of the rabbet throat.

The lower side of the large circular opening on the left side of the stock is joined to the mouth sawcut, by scribing a tangent straight line segment. The elevation of this joining should be $\frac{13}{16}$" above the bottom of the blank. (A rabbet will later remove the lower $\frac{1}{2}$" of the left side of the stock, leaving the bottom of the rabbet curve $\frac{5}{16}$" above the deepest dado cut.) Cut along this line, continuing the sweep of the conical hole, to complete the roughing of the throat. The stock at this point appears as in the third sketch of Fig.15:5.

In front of the place where the wedge mortise enters the top of the conical opening, the wood presents a region of short grain. It is very easy to split this out, leaving an unsightly scar, in the process of forming the mortise. The front of this entry point should be deeply scribed with a thin chisel extended up from the mouth opening, as shown in the bottom sketch of Fig.15:5. If possible, break through into the drill hole before further cutting from the top of the stock. The more of this lower opening that can be cut from below, the less the danger of splitout. The narrow mouth opening restricts your freedom, and requires care to avoid marring the mouth front.

The Japanese type compass saw is useful in extending the wedge mortise into its sharp skew corners. As it cuts on the pull stroke, it is less apt to cause damage in this area when sawing from the top of the stock. The wedge mortise is continued with

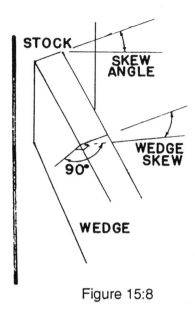

Figure 15:8

bevel-sided paring chisels, guided by the layout lines. The rear of the mortise should be flat, and a continuation of the plane established by the initial saw cut. A triangular float is of great help in completing this opening, and you should consider making one (p.82) if the task becomes onerous.

WEDGE The wedge is now started. A blank is cut to the thickness of the wedge mortise, tapered to the mortise angle, and front and back of the wedge are planed to match the skew angle. Be aware that the slope of the wedge mortise alters the angles required at the front and back of the wedge, making these smaller than the skew angle (see Fig.15:8). They are closer to 15° on the back of the wedge, 17° on the front. (See the Appendix if you wish to calculate these for your plane). Both wedge and mortise are pared and trimmed to fit, as has been described in earlier chapters. Remember that the greatest pressure should bear on the iron as near to the cutting edge as possible. With wedge and iron installed, mark the lower edge of the wedge with a vertical line at a point which allows at least the same clearance for shavings between it and the throat front as is allowed at the mouth. Cut along this line, slanting the cut forward in the horizontal plane to agree with the skew of the throat front, as seen in Fig.15:9.

The mortise for the nicker iron is now laid out and cut. It is $\frac{3}{8}$"

Figure 15:9

wide, centered on top of the stock, $\frac{7}{8}$" from the toe and $\frac{3}{4}$" long. The rear is vertical, the front tapered back at 10°. This is drilled (or mortised with the mortising attachment) as far as the taper permits ($2\frac{1}{2}$"). The front face of the mortise is started with a $\frac{3}{8}$" mortise chisel, but the depth reached by this, too, is limited by its thickness.

The rear wall of the nicker mortise must be extended to the right to accommodate the wide section of the nicker iron, as sketched in Fig.15:7. This extension takes the form of a slit penetrating the right side of the stock, $\frac{1}{8}$" wide and extending $1\frac{3}{4}$" up from the sole. It is convenient to form this now, to facilitate completion of the upper wedge mortise. The cut may be started on the table saw, with the stock on its right side and using a stop to avoid overcutting. It is completed with a $\frac{1}{8}$" mortise chisel and a thin paring chisel. Drilling upward through this slit with a $\frac{1}{8}$" long shank drill facilitates the completion of the nicker mortise, with paring chisels. The nicker wedge is made in a manner familiar to you by now.

We have delayed cutting the rabbet in the left side and sole of the stock until this point, to have a solid base available on the body for the mortising operations. It may now be cut on the table saw, cutting upward $\frac{1}{2}$" and leaving $\frac{13}{16}$" for the sole. (This, of course, is controlled by the width of your iron.) This thickness allows both sides of the main iron to protrude very slightly beyond the sole.

DEPTH STOP Early dado planes had a simple depth stop, a wooden bar held in a vertical mortise through the stock with a friction fit. An improvement in this type added a wooden screw, bearing on the side of the stop, threaded through the stock side. (If you choose to use a wooden stop, the mortise for it is made in the same manner as described below for the metal one.) Later, a brass side stop was used, a slotted brass casting screwed to the side of the stock. The best dado planes used metal stops adjustable by a thumbscrew. These were not made by the planemaker; he purchased them from a hardware supplier. Metal depth stops of the various types were listed in catalogs, as early as the 1829 John Wilk's and as late as 1909 in Preston's. Unfortunately, we cannot order these today. You may be able to find a depth stop mechanism recovered from a damaged dado. If not, one must be made.

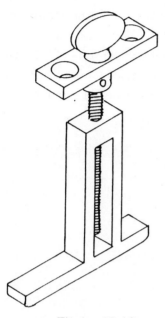

Figure 15:10

The prototype used an iron depth stop of the type shown in Fig. 15:10, adjusted with a ¼"-24 thread. This is not beyond the scope of a home workshop, if you enjoy cutting, drilling and filing boiler plate. I chose to use an earlier method of construction, commonly found in earlier dados, and copied a depth stop used by the Gabriel firm (1770-1822) in one of their dados. This unites a shaft and foot, both made of bar stock. My version is shown in Fig. 15:11.

The shaft is made from a two inch length of ¼ x ⅝" brass bar stock. This is drilled through its center, lengthwise, with a tap drill for about ½", and with a drill sized to clear the adjustment screw thread for the rest of the way (the procedure used is described on p.95).

The foot is made from two inches of ³⁄₁₆ x ⅜" bar stock, having its front and rear lower edges rounded. The foot is not centered on the shaft, but extends forward just beyond the point where the nicker protrudes. The shaft is located ⁵⁄₁₆" from the end of the foot, and aligns with one side of it as shown in the sketch. The foot of the depth stops of authentic planes is almost invariably made of iron. I perversely choose to use brass, for appearance. The shaft and foot of the Gabriel depth stop (and others like it) were joined with a steel pin forced through mating holes in each, presumably peened and filed flat on the bottom of the foot. I have used this in other stops, but choose the easier way of soldering them together. Use silver solder if you are familiar with this process, or as a minimum a strong tin-silver solder which handles like the common lead-tin material.

A bearing plate is made from the same stock as the shaft, centrally drilled to clear the 10-24 screw and having two screw holes drilled and countersunk for mounting. A knurled adjustment knob, a departure from the prototype but easier to make, is turned on a lathe from ⅝" brass rod. (You may prefer to hand-file a brass thumbscrew head to match your prototype.) It is drilled partly through, tapped, and fitted with a 2½" length of 10-24 threaded rod screwed tightly home and soldered in place. This is passed through the central hole in the bearing plate, and a nut threaded onto it for a close but free-turning fit in the plate. The nut is a short length of brass rod tapped to fit the adjustment screw. It is secured in position by drilling through both the nut and the threaded rod with a #50 or smaller drill, and pinning with a very thin brad or length of iron wire.

One more mortise is needed in the stock, to mount this depth stop. It is vertical, ¼ x ⅝" in section, penetrating the stock 2⅜" back of the toe and with its right side aligned with the side of the rabbet cut in the sole (see Fig.

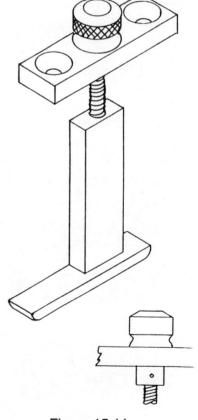

Figure 15:11

15:4). In the absence of a mortising attachment, it may be started by drilling two ¼" holes from the sole to the top of the stock, and finished with a ¼" mortise chisel and a float (or file). It should provide a close but sliding fit with the metal shaft of the depth stop.

The foot of the depth stop is to be recessed into the stock, to allow for the full range of adjustment. The bearing plate must be inlet into the top of the stock. With the stop mechanism in place, scribe outlines for both of these and sink them with an end mill (or chisel and router, if you prefer). Drill pilot holes for the bearing plate mounting screws, prefer-ably using a Vix bit which automatically centers the pilot holes within the countersink.

The iron is now sharpened, taking care to make the cutting edge match the sole profile when the iron is set to extend just beyond the stock on either side. Some adjustment of its skew angle will probably be required for this fit. The spurs of the nicker iron are sharpened to knife edges, making sure that they are spaced exactly in front of the two sides of the main cutter. After two coats of linseed oil or other finish of your choice, your dado is ready for assembly and fettling.

CHAPTER 16

WEDGE-ARM FILLETSTER

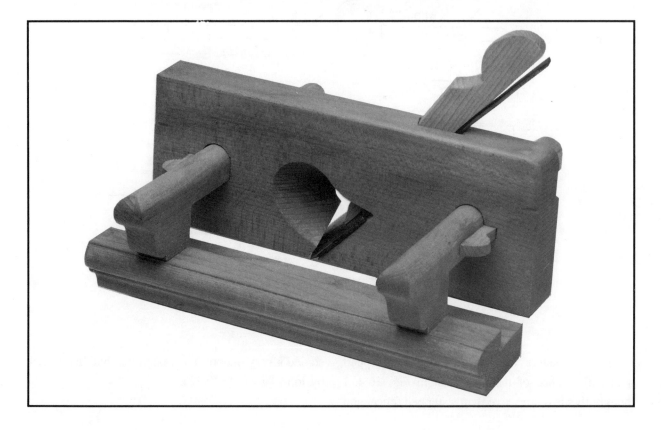

The most common method of supporting a movable fence on plows and similar planes (at least in the English-speaking world) is by arms attached to the fence, passing through the stock, and fixed in position by wedges (called keys) bearing on the sides of the arms. Most often seen with this suspension are plow planes (Fig. 16:1). However, since we shall see three variants of the plow plane in subsequent chapters, another plane type was chosen to illustrate the wedge-arm fence. In addition, wedge-arm plows are plentiful and inexpensive, while the arm filletsters are not.

The word "filletster" is still spelled this way in the U.S., although the English abandoned this for "fillister" many years ago. We have, however, accepted their pronunciation, with the first "t" silent. These planes are used for making rabbets, square grooves cutting away part of the face and edge of a board. The standing filletster (right, Fig. 16:2) has a fixed fence cut in the material of the stock; its neighbor on the left of the figure having a fixed depth stop set to cut a square rabbet is called a halving plane. The moving filletster (Fig. 16:3; the "moving" is usually omitted in the U.S., as standing filletsters are rare) is most often found with a simple movable fence screwed to the sole of the stock and an adjustable depth stop; it will cut rabbets of various sizes. Some are seen with fences supported on screw-arms; less often, they are found with fences on wedge arms. The more common sash filletster should not be confused with the wedge-arm or screw-arm filletster; the former is designed to cut a rabbet on the far side of the workpiece, and has its nicker on the left side of the stock. It was used to cut the rabbet in window sash bars (to hold the glass) on the far side of the bar, to avoid repositioning the bar for the molding operation.

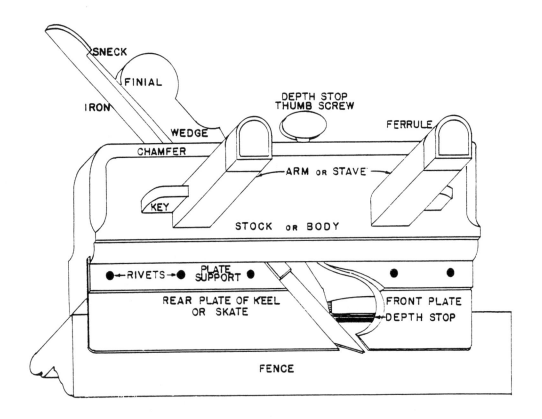

Figure 16:1

Arm filletsters were almost always equipped with a flat fence of the type seen in Fig. 16:4. I thought this less attractive than a stepped fence, and copied a very uncommon design that had been used by John Taber (1820-72).

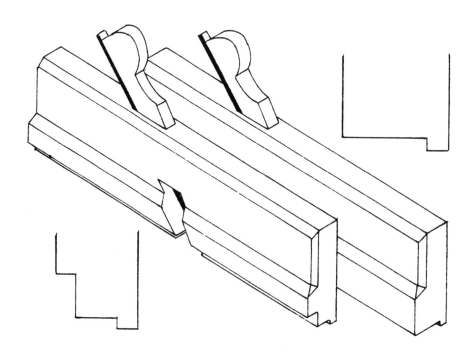

Figure 16:2

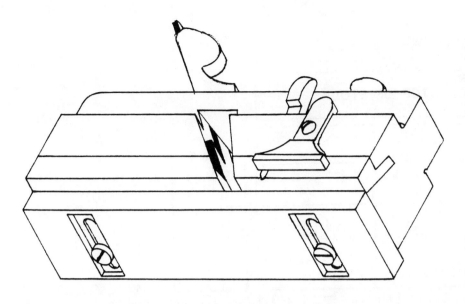

Figure 16:3

IRON An old skew blade having a central tang and a cutting edge $1\frac{1}{2}$" wide was located, wider but similar in shape to the one used for the dado of the last chapter. It was rejuvenated by the now familiar procedure described there.

LAYOUT Dimensioned orthographic projections of the parts of this plane are given in Fig. 16:5, if you find these easier to follow than text. The initial steps forming the throat and wedge mortise of the present stock are quite similar to those used in making the dado of the last chapter. The instructions will be repeated where there are minor differences in dimension, with reference to the previous chapter when they are identical.

A block of beechwood is squared to $9\frac{1}{2}$ x $3\frac{1}{2}$ x $1\frac{3}{8}$ ". The bed line is scribed on the sole 4" back from the toe on the right side of the stock, angling back toward the heel at 20°. Bedlines are marked on the sides at a bed angle of 45°, and joined across the top of the stock. A

parallel line 1" forward of this marks the front of the wedge mortise, and the sides are marked to center the $\frac{1}{2}$ " wide mortise in the stock. The front of the mouth is marked on the sole, $\frac{1}{4}$" forward of and parallel to the bedline. Lines on the stock sides join this mouth line to the ends of the lines marking the front of the mortise outline on top of the stock.

THROAT The rabbet type throat is begun as a $\frac{5}{8}$" hole bored through the stock from a center on the right side of the stock $4\frac{1}{4}$" back from the toe and up $1\frac{1}{4}$" from the sole. The hole is angled forward and up, to emerge centered about 4" from the toe and $1\frac{1}{2}$" above the sole (the angle is not particularly critical). It is enlarged with a pipe reamer, as described in the dado chapter. Cut along the lower bedline (kerf between bed and mouth) with a bench saw, with the tilt angle set at just over 43° and the miter gauge at 20°, terminating the cut $1\frac{3}{8}$" above the sole. The front of the throat is

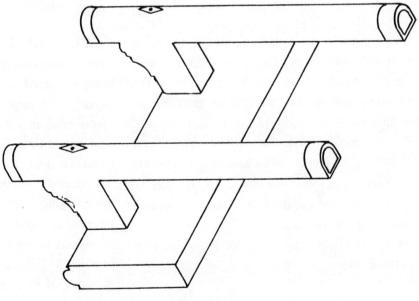

Figure 16:4

81

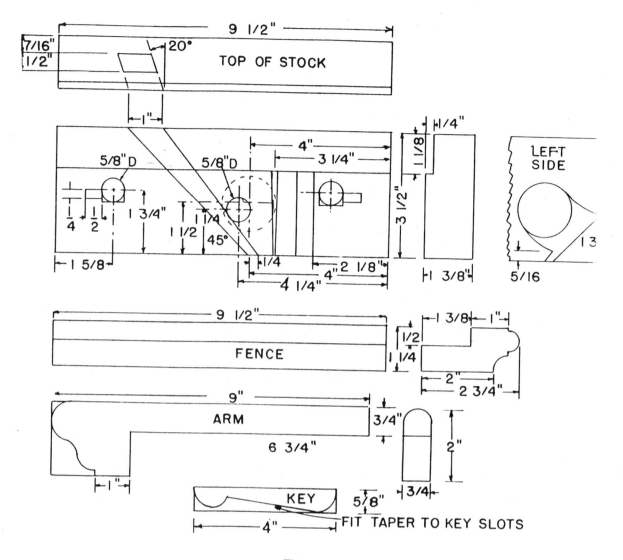

Figure 16:5

similarly cut with tilt angle just over 36° and miter still at 20°, with blade exposure reduced to avoid cutting into the upper edge of the conical hole. The cuts joining this hole to the sawcuts are made as described and pictured (Fig. 15.5) in the dado chapter, with the exception (since there will be no rabbet cut in the sole of this plane) that the lower arc dips further down to meet the throat front $5/16$" above the sole.

The wedge mortise is cut by the same procedure as described for the dado (pp. 75-76), but was much more easily effected by using the triangular float described below.

TRIANGULAR FLOAT Recalling the problems encountered in finishing the mortise for a skew blade it seemed desirable to make a float capable of handling the acute angles. This was done, and is recommended; the time saved by its use almost equalled the time spent in making a rough-and-ready triangular float.

An old 7" three-square (triangular) file is annealed by heating to redness in a propane torch and covering it with agricultural lime or fireplace ash to allow it to cool slowly. The teeth are ground off from one face, and this surface is leveled with a belt sander. A series of crosswise notches are made, equally spaced along its length, with a hacksaw. These were

82

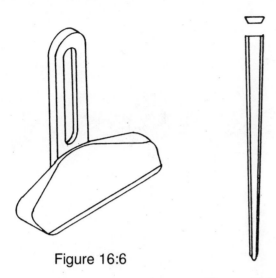

Figure 16:6

Figure 16:7

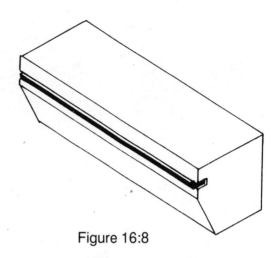

Figure 16:8

converted to teeth profiled like a ripsaw's by use of large triangular files (rough, then fine), as described on p.61.

WEDGE A wedge blank is cut from beech, $\frac{1}{2}$ x $1\frac{1}{4}$ x 7" and tapered to fit both the mortise angle and the skew angle. Remember that the skew angle at the front and back of the wedge is not equal to the skew angle seen on top of the stock, because of the pitch (see Fig. 15:8 of the previous chapter). It is approximately 16° in front, 14° in back of the wedge.

Continue paring the mortise and adjusting the wedge until a good fit is obtained with wedge and iron in place. Be sure that the wedge exerts pressure near the cutting edge of the iron. The lower end of the wedge is shaped as shown in Fig. 15:9, and the finial is shaped as you please.

DEPTH STOP A depth stop of the type referred to as a brass side stop can sometimes be provided by an antique tool dealer. Lacking this, a satisfactory substitute can be made from brass bar stock (Fig. 16:6). A two-inch length of $\frac{1}{2}$ x $\frac{1}{2}$" bar is shaped into the foot with hacksaw and files, and the arm is cut from two inches of $\frac{1}{8}$ x $\frac{1}{2}$" bar. The screw slot is made by drilling two $\frac{3}{16}$" holes at its ends, and removing the material between them (a jeweler's saw works well). The foot and arm may be united by any of several methods (I used silver-bearing solder), taking care that the arm is at right angles to the bearing surface of the foot.

The vertical dado in the stock which guides the depth stop is located forward of the mouth, at a position which puts the rear of the depth stop foot about $\frac{1}{4}$" in front of the mouth. It is cut in the right side of the stock, to a depth just short of the thickness of the brass arm and wide enough for a sliding fit with the depth stop arm. A small router such as the Stanley 271 helps to finish this. The usual means of tightening the depth stop is a cheese-head or filletster head wood screw. Lacking this, I made a substitute by lathe-turning a brass washer, countersunk to fit a flat-head wood screw, to act as the bearing surface. A round-head screw will, of course, serve.

NICKER The nicker iron is retained in a doubly tapered slot in the stock. Two views of this iron are given in Fig. 16:7. It is made from tool steel $\frac{3}{32}$" thick, a 3" length being cut to taper in width from $\frac{1}{4}$" to $\frac{5}{32}$". The nicker is given a trapezoidal cross-section by tapering both sides at about 60°. It is an awkward piece to hold for this operation. A method which works well is to force the nicker blank into a slot cut in a piece of hardwood, which holds it at a suitable distance above the guide of a grinding wheel, and traversing the piece across the wheel (Fig. 16:8). (You can, of course, cut the blank long leaving room to hold it by both ends during grinding.) Hardening, shaping and sharpening is deferred until the slot is cut in the stock and a fit is obtained.

A shoulder is now made in the right side of the stock, to provide for more convenient adjustment of

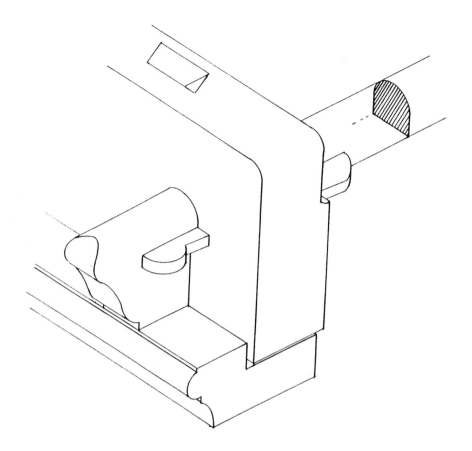

Figure 16:9

the nicker. Two bench saw cuts remove $\frac{1}{4}$" of width, $1\frac{1}{8}$" from the top of the stock. This is smoothed with a scraper, and the step is coved with a small round molding plane. The tapered vertical slot in the stock to hold the nicker blade is made to the rear of the depth stop dado, located to place the point of the nicker just under the foot of the depth stop. It is made by two thin-kerf bench saw cuts carefully set (by trial cuts on scrap) to the exact depth of the nicker thickness, and spaced to match the width of the nicker blade on its outer (narrower) surface. The slot is carefully tapered inward with chisels to match the taper of the nicker sides. A triangular needle file helps to fit the nicker into this slot, carefully widening it until the tip of the nicker just passes beyond the sole of the stock. After achieving this, the nicker may be hardened (as described in Chapter 23) and sharpened, only the the inner (wider) side of the nicker being bevelled.

ARMS The fence arms are made from a length of beech a full $\frac{3}{4}$" thick and 2" wide. One edge of this is shaped into a true semicircle. Two passes of a $\frac{3}{8}$" roundover bit in a power router accomplishes this quickly, but hollow planes followed by a scraper filed to the proper profile will serve. Two 9" lengths are cut off, and the arms formed by sawing away all but $\frac{3}{4}$" for $6\frac{3}{4}$", leaving as cross-section a $\frac{3}{4}$" square with the top rounded into a semicircle. At the end of this cut a cross-cut forms the inner side of the shoulder (see Figs. 16:5 and 16:9). Molding the outer sides of the shoulders is deferred until later.

The holes in the stock to take the arms are now made. Begin with a $\frac{3}{4}$" Forstner bit in a drill press (the holes must be exactly perpendicular to the sides of the stock). Center the two holes $1\frac{3}{4}$" above the sole, $1\frac{5}{8}$" away from the toe and the heel. Scribe a line parallel to the sole tangent to the bottom of these holes, and lines perpendicular to the sole tangent to either side. Remove the waste with a sharp chisel and floats to exactly fit the arms. Slots for the arm keys are cut in the outer side of these holes, $\frac{1}{4}$" wide, extending $\frac{1}{4}$" from the hole on the left side of the stock and tapering out to $\frac{1}{2}$" on the right. Continue fitting the armholes until a smooth but snug sliding fit is won. Make sure that the arms are perpendicular to the stock when fitting is complete.

FENCE   The fence is made from a $1\frac{1}{4}$ x $2\frac{3}{4}$ x $9\frac{1}{2}$" squared block of beech. A rabbet is sawn away, $\frac{1}{2}$ x $1\frac{3}{8}$", to allow the fence to slip under the stock. (If you prefer the classical fence, a uniform $\frac{3}{4}$" thick, the shoulders on your arms must be made longer than specified above.)

The outer side of the fence may now be molded to please your fancy. The tool of the photograph has 1" of width left on the upper surface of the fence to bear the arm shoulders, after cutting an astragal and cove (Fig. 16:9).

After finishing the sole of the stock, making sure that it remains square to the sides and is perfectly flat, insert the arms. Place the fence rabbet against the sole and mark the bottom of the arm shoulders at the level of the top surface of the fence. Cut away the excess shoulder below this mark, leaving a margin for final adjustment. Mark the bottom of the shoulders to match the width of the top surface of the fence. The outer sides of the shoulders may now be molded as you please (a fillet and double ogee is illustrated).

With arms fully inserted into the stock, check the clearance between fence and sole with the fence held tightly against the shoulders of the arms. Make sure that the shoulders fit squarely on the fence; any tilt will harm the sliding action. Pare the bottoms of the shoulders carefully until they exactly fit the fence surface, and the small clearance ($\frac{1}{64}$" or so) between fence and sole is uniform. Be fussy at this point. Inaccuracy here will require an unpleasant increase in the size of the arm holes.

Mark the location of the shoulders of the arms on the fence surface, and locate centers for the screw holes. Drill the fence (in a press) for this, to suit the screw to be used (mine are $1\frac{3}{4}$" #10 flathead) and countersink the lower fence surface. Mark and centerpunch the shoulder of one arm and drill the pilot hole for the screw. Screw the arm to the fence and insert it into the stock. With the second arm inserted into the stock and aligned in its final position on the fence, clamp it in position and drill its pilot hole. Care in this operation will be rewarded with a smoothly adjustable fence. Screw this arm in place, and reap the reward.

The keys which fix the arms in place are cut from $\frac{1}{4}$" beech, tapered to match their slots in the stock and enlarged at the small end to prevent their escape during adjustments. They are inserted in their slots before the arms are inserted.

All that remains to be done is finish scraping of the surfaces, and chamfering the upper edges as you prefer. As always, the top rear should be rounded for a comfortable grip. The plane of the illustration was finished with two coats of tung oil, and waxed.

CHAPTER 17

PLOW PLANES: THE BRIDLE PLOW

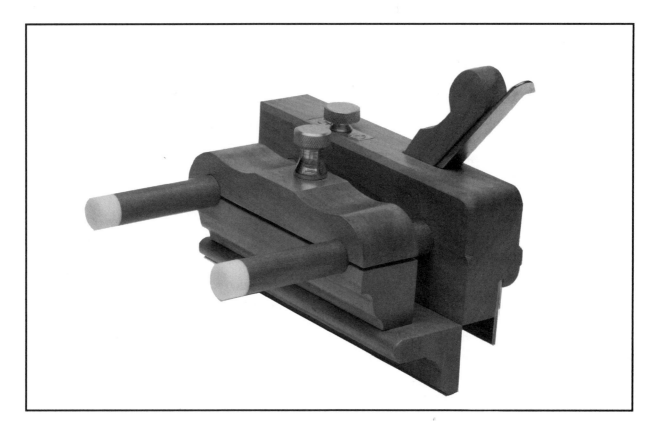

The plow plane is used to sink grooves at a distance from the edge of a workpiece. The path of its cutting edge is controlled by a fence, which is kept in contact with the edge of the work being grooved. The distance between fence and cutting edge determines the location of the groove to be cut, and this distance is adjustable. A typical application was cutting grooves in framing to hold the panels of paneled walls or doors.

Plows may be equipped with a set (commonly eight) of interchangeable plow irons to permit cutting groove widths from $\frac{1}{8}$" to $\frac{5}{8}$". However, most surviving plows are found with just one iron, the one mounted in the plane; the rest of the set having been misplaced over the years. Fortunately, unlike many tools of their vintage, the plow irons were fairly standard in size, and are generally usable in more

than one plow. Loose irons are often available from antique tool sources (sometimes even in complete sets by one maker), so that finding them for your tool is not too difficult.

All plow irons of a set have their upper portion at the same width, to fit the wedge mortise, but their lower section is reduced to the width of the cutting edge (Fig. 17:1). This end of the iron, when mounted in the plow, is supported from the rear by an iron skate (keel) fixed to the stock. The heel section of the skate has its forward edge sloped at the bed angle of the stock, and beveled to a V-shape. This fits into a V-groove in the lower back of the iron, supporting it and preventing sidewise displacement. The skate must, of course, be no wider than the narrowest groove to be cut. Thus, the forward section of the skate presses on only a portion of the wood in front of the cutting edge. It cannot provide an effective

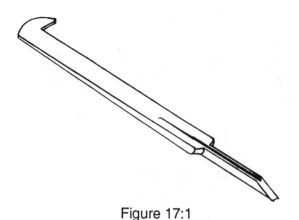

Figure 17:1

mouth for the wider irons, and thus the plow produces a rougher cut than other types of plane. This is of little importance at the bottom of a groove.

In using the plow to cut the narrower grooves, it is necessary for the fence to be accurately aligned parallel to the skate; otherwise the skate would rub on the sides of the cut. Some early New England plows (the "Yankee" plows) use a rigid attachment of the arms to the fence, in which the arm shoulders are inset into dados in the fence. This ensures that fence and skate remain parallel, but makes adjustment burdensome. Later makers of plows using either the wedge arm suspension treated in the last chapter, or the screw arms to be seen later, abandoned this practice. Their tools allow the arms to pivot around the rivet or screw holding them to the fence. Being able to move the arms one at a time makes their adjustment easier, especially for the wedge arm type whose arms frequently bind. However, doing so means that the arms require individual adjustment to make the fence parallel to the skate.

Over the years, many variations in the fence support system were tried to accomplish the fence-to-skate alignment automatically. The most popular of these were variants of the bridle plow, in which the arms are fixed permanently in the stock. The fence is tightened on both arms simultaneously by a clamp (the bridle) in such a way that correct alignment was enforced. The earliest designs used a wooden bridle, but metal bridles are more often seen. The particular design sketched in Fig. 17:2 (a plow by McGlashan, 1827-1849) relies on the V-grooves in the fence to ensure fence alignment. The plow shown in the photograph has a bridle structure which completely surrounds the arms for this purpose.

The model for the body and fence of the present tool was a conventional plow by Cauldwall (Birmingham, England, 1798-1821). The bridle assembly is my own interpretation. All wooden parts are applewood, and the plow irons were chosen from a collection accumulated over the years from antique tool dealers.

STOCK Dimensioned orthographic drawings for the various parts of this tool are given in Fig. 17:3. A blank for the stock is squared to 7¾ x 3 x 1¾". An

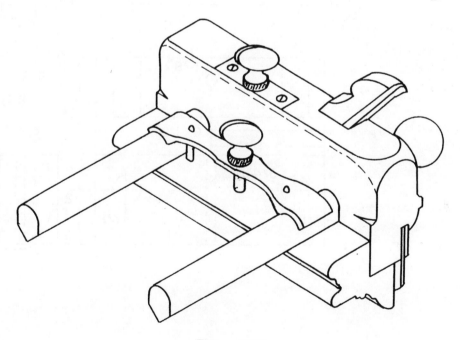

Figure 17:2

87

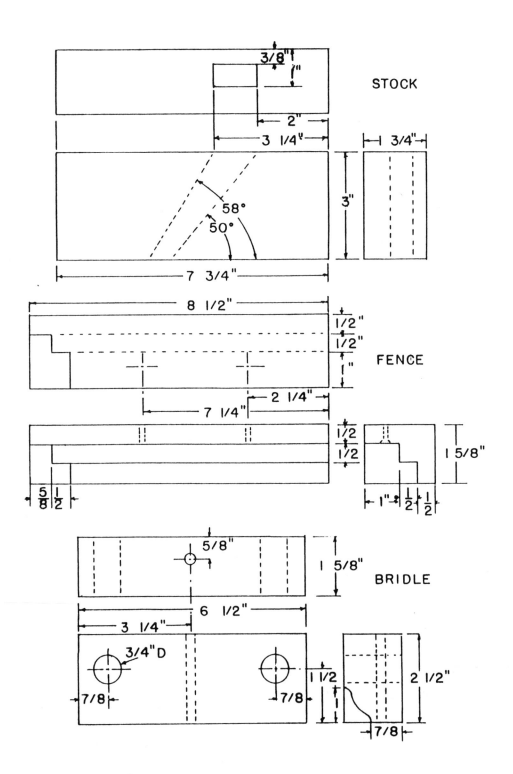

Figure 17:3

88

isometric view of the layout lines is seen in Fig. 17:4. The mortise for iron and wedge is laid out on top of the blank, lines 2" and 3¼" from the heel for back and front, 1" and ⅜" from the right side of the

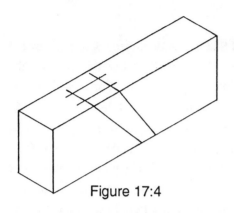

Figure 17:4

stock for the mortise sides. The bed line at the rear of the mortise is laid out on the right side of the stock, at 50° (York pitch) from the horizontal, and the front of the mortise is marked by a line at 58°.

WEDGE MORTISE Although we have covered this operation several times before, it bears repeating here with specifics for plow planes. Begin the mortise by sinking its layout lines on the upper surface with a sharp chisel, and cut a surface at right angles to the bed line to provide a secure starting point for drilling. Center punch on the center line of this outline, ⁵⁄₁₆" from the bedline. A drill press ensures accurate drilling if the stock is supported in a simple jig, similar to Fig.12:8 in Chapter 12. (If you prefer to drill by hand, use a smaller drill and great care.)

The jig consists of two square sides, on one of which battens are mounted to support sole and toe of the stock at the proper angle to make the bedline exactly vertical. The two sides of the jig are clamped together with the stock between them, sole and toe in contact with the battens. Take great care in clamping and positioning the assembly for drilling, that the sides of the jig are upright, at an exact right angle to the table of the drill press. Using a ⅝" drill bit, bore to a depth just short of breaking through the lower surface of the stock. This hole is now tangent to the bedline and the two sides of the mortise, and provides guidelines for the chisels to follow. The hole is com-

pleted by breaking through from the underside with chisels, perhaps with assistance from a smaller diameter drill.

The waste in front of this hole is removed with a mortise chisel to approach the desired front surface, indicated by the forward layout line. The task is completed with paring chisels and floats (see p.61). The objective is a truly flat surface for the iron to rest on, an opening wide enough to accept the plow irons, and a flat bearing surface for the front of the wedge. The performance of the final tool rests heavily on reaching this objective, so be generous with the time allotted. If you have not previously cut a wedge mortise, it is good insurance to practise on scrap wood.

WEDGE This is required for future layout, and is fitted now. A blank is cut to a thickness of ⅝", at least 1⅛" wide and long enough (about 8") to provide a margin of safety for fitting adjustments. The end of the blank is tapered at the approximate angle required; that is, the mortise angle plus the angle of the plow iron (usually a bit under 2°) or about 10°. Insert wedge and iron in the mortise (paring the mortise sides may be required). Trim the wedge angle until it contacts both iron and the front of the mortise over its full length, and seats the iron firmly with a light tap on its top. Aim for applying greatest pressure on the lower end of the iron. Final fitting and shaping the finial and wedge bottom may be deferred until the skate is installed.

SKATE LOCATION The skate is to be positioned in line with the center of the wedge mortise, and screwed to the side of a rabbet in the stock side. The top of the skate, and its associated sole plate, have their top edges sunk into a groove at the top of this rabbet. The classic procedure was to rabbet the stock first, then cut the groove with a plow; this should be used if you work by hand. An alternate sequence used here, useful with the table saw, is to cut the groove first, to full height, then remove the side of the rabbet.

Wedge the iron in place, centered in its mortise

if there is any play. Mark on the sole the location of the midpoint of the plow iron (at the groove in the rear of the iron). Carry this location back to the heel of the stock (left, Fig. 17:5). Scribe lines on the heel for the skate location, separated by the thickness of the skate material and centered on this location. (The present plane uses flat ground steel stock, $3/32$ x $1^1/_2$", for the skate, and 14 gauge (.064") brass $^{11}/_{16}$" wide for the sole plate covering its top. A groove width of about .158" is required to accept these.) A second line is scribed, the thickness of the sole plate to the right of the right line, to locate the right edge of the groove to be cut. The table saw blade is set to true vertical and the rip fence is set (right side of the stock against it) to cut just on the line marking the inner edge of the skate. The cut is $7/_8$" deep. The groove is widened to the combined thickness of your skate and sole plate, by a second pass of the saw blade. The stock at this point is shown in the center sketch of Fig. 17:5. It is safer to leave the fence untouched and shim the stock to get the correct groove width, rather than trying to get an exact width by rip fence adjustment. The right side of the groove, except for the top $1/_8$", is now cut away to complete the rabbet (along the dotted line of the center sketch, 17:5). The lower right side of the stock, above this rabbet, may now be molded as you please (with a quarter round plane in the plow illustrated), as shown in the right sketch of Fig. 17:5.

DEPTH STOP A depth stop was made by the procedure described at the end of this chapter, the foot dimensions as given there. For this plow, the shaft was made from a two inch length of $1/_4$ x $5/_8$" brass bar stock, as I was too impatient to wait for thicker material. It was drilled and tapped for a 10-24 thread. The foot was attached by pinning with a short length of brass rod forced into the hole in the bottom of the shaft and through a hole in the foot, supplemented by soft soldering. The knurled knob seen in the photograph and in Fig.17:6 was lathe turned from $7/_8$" brass rod.

The foot of your depth stop (except for the cutout which clears the plow iron) should almost touch the skate, which locates the lateral position of the depth stop mortise. The upright shaft should be located just in front of the wedge mortise. (In the present plane, this placed the front of the shaft $2^3/_{16}$" back from the toe.) With the location of the mortise for the depth stop shaft established, it is marked on top of the stock, outlined with a chisel, drilled, and cleared with chisel and float. Fit it to the depth stop shaft until this slides

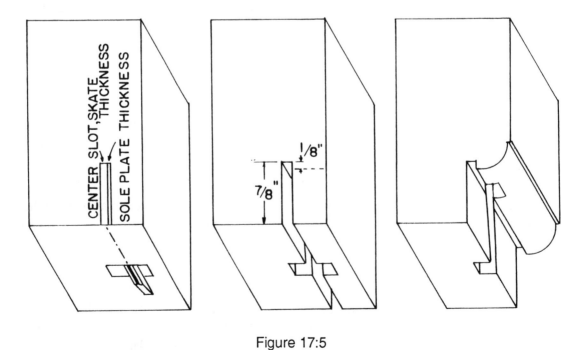

Figure 17:5

90

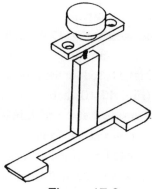

Figure 17:6

freely without lateral movement. The top of this mortise may have to be enlarged to allow room for the bulge of the retaining washer below the bearing plate of the depth stop mechanism.

Insert the upright of the stop into its mortise and scribe the outline of the foot on the bottom of the stock. Inlet to allow the foot to retract its full thickness into the stock, using either an end mill (p.38) or chisel and hand router. The position of the foot after inletting is seen in Fig.17:7. Replace the shaft of the stop in its mortise and thread the adjustment screw into it. Mark the outline of its bearing plate on the top of the stock. Cut the recess to inlet the bearing plate level with the top of the stock, with chisel and hand router. Drill pilot holes for its mounting screws. It is good practice to make a mark indicating the front end of the bearing plate on its hidden underside after its recess is cut. Neither the old plates nor ones we make can be relied upon to be interchangeable end for end.

SKATE   The rear skate section is made by cutting one end of the steel strip described above at 50° (or the exact angle of the back of the wedge mortise, if this has drifted a bit from the layout line). Bevel this edge on both sides to fit the V-groove in the lower back of your plow iron. Old plows usually have the bevel cut back, above the level of the sole plate, to accommodate irons whose groove thins out at the upper end. Check the fit with the skate and sole

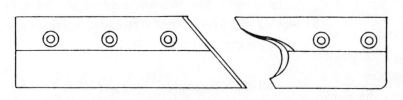

Figure 17:8

plate inserted in their groove and the iron wedged in place. This must be good. Unless the lower end of the iron is supported, the cut is subject to chatter. Any misalignment is corrected, and the rear skate section is marked and cut to length.

The same steel stock is used for the front section of the skate. It has its after end shaped for shavings clearance as in Fig.17:8 (a jeweler's saw and files serve). Note that the curved edge is beveled on the exposed side, to avoid hindrance to shavings escape. With the plow iron wedged into cutting position, this skate section is inserted in its groove and adjusted to

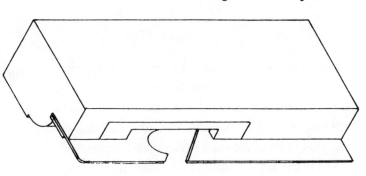

Figure 17:7

allow ⅛" or a bit less (for shavings clearance) between its bottom edge and the cutting edge of the iron. The location of the front of the stock is marked on the skate, and it is cut to length at this mark. Its front lower corner is rounded slightly to avoid gouging the work.

The brass strip for the sole plate is scribed to match the tops of the two steel skate sections, and cut to fit. The outer side of the front section is shaped to continue the bevel of the curve in its steel mate (Fig.17:8). The steel and brass members are held together in pairs while drilling and countersinking for #10 x ¾" wood screws, two in the front section of the skate, three in the rear. (Most plows have their sole plate and skate permanently connected by brass pins or otherwise, and were presumably shaped together.) With the iron wedged in place and both steel and brass parts of the rear skate installed in their groove, the skate is adjusted longitudinally for

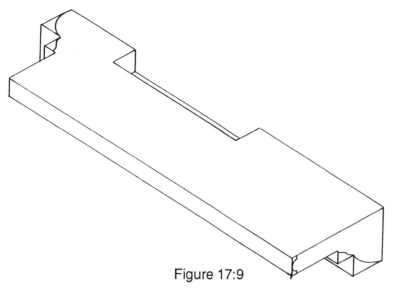

Figure 17:9

proper support of the iron. The location of the pilot hole for the screw nearest the toe is marked and drilled. Drive this screw home, then mark and drill the other two screw holes. A VIX bit, which locates the pilot holes at the exact center of the countersunk holes in the skate, helps to make these fit precisely; a misaligned screw head detracts considerably from the appearance of the tool. Repeat for the front skate section. While the front skate is in position, scribe the stock exposed behind it (just in front of the wedge mortise) with the outline of the skate's curve. Pare the wood of the stock to the scribed outline, continuing the bevel of the skate and sole plate, for easy shavings escape. Defer mounting the skate until the wooden parts are finished and oiled.

FENCE A block of the same wood as the stock is squared to $1\frac{5}{8}$ x 2 x $8\frac{1}{2}$". Align this block with the heel of the stock and mark the location of the cutout for the depth stop recess, as shown in Fig. 17:9. This is sized to permit the fence to reach the skate, with the depth stop at its lowest position. The recess is sunk, with end mill and chisel or with chisel and hand router.

Sketch the molding profile you would like to use on the heel of the fence. A thickness of $\frac{1}{2}$" is adequate for the right and bottom extensions of this member. The side molding profile turns the corner and the pattern is repeated, rising up the front of the

fence. Cut rabbets to eliminate the waste, as shown in the sketch (Fig. 17:9). Rabbets down the front are done with the same saw settings as used for the rabbets on the side (Fig. 17:10; accuracy is needed here to ensure that the moldings meet in a clean miter at the front). The moldings are now to be formed ("stuck" is the old verb) on the side and front of the fence.

Professional planemakers molded the front of the fence in batches of four or more, clamping them tightly together with the last one backed up by scrap wood. Using molding planes cross-grain invites splitting out the wood as the cutting edge leaves the workpiece, and the scrap protects the last piece. Doing several at a time provides a more stable

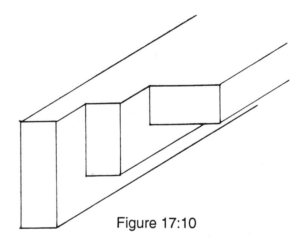

Figure 17:10

footing for the molders. As you and I make one at a time, this is not too practical. There are a number of alternatives, but one which served me is to cut the profile on the side of the fence first with round and hollow planes, then rough out the same pattern on the front with a bandsaw, and finish with gouges, chisels and files. Use care to ensure clean meetings at the miter corners. The leftmost edge of the fence is molded with a center bead. The completed fence and bridle are sketched in Fig. 17:11.

ARMS These are 6" long and $\frac{3}{4}$" in diameter. The diameter must correspond accurately with the

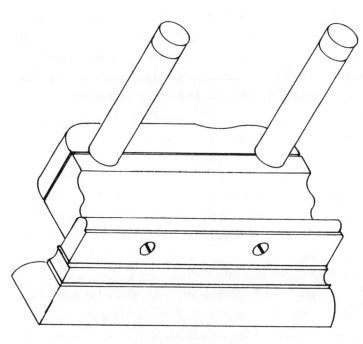

Figure 17:11

table is exactly perpendicular to the drill, and that the table is free of shavings.

The bridle is positioned with its lower edge just a bit (about $\frac{1}{64}$") below the bottom of the plow body, and its heel end $\frac{5}{8}$" forward of the heel of the stock. The location of one of the armholes in the bridle is carefully transcribed to the plow body, and an armhole drilled in it using the same bit as used on the bridle, to a depth of $\frac{3}{4}$". After drilling the first hole, the body and bridle are connected by forcing one of the arms through the bridle and into this hole. The body and bridle are carefully aligned, and the second hole drilled in the body with the bit passing through the hole in the bridle. This procedure seems cumbersome, but guarantees precise arm location.

Provision is now made for tightening the bridle on the arms. A $\frac{1}{4}$" hole is drilled from top to bottom through the bridle block, $\frac{5}{8}$" from the body side and centered on its length, to contain the adjustment screw. The bridle block may now be cut apart, in a plane precisely through the center lines of the arm holes.

With the fence positioned on the stock just clearing the skate groove, measure the width of the exposed flat section on the top surface of the fence to which the bridle will be attached ($\frac{7}{8}$" in the plane shown). The thickness at the bottom of the lower portion of the bridle must be reduced to conform to this measurement by molding its outboard side (I used a "humpback" or double ogee cut with hollows and rounds). A 3" hex-head (or square-head) $\frac{1}{4}$" bolt is inserted through the bottom of the $\frac{1}{4}$" hole, and the wood marked to inlet the head into the bridle base. The head must be sunk to its full thickness, no further, and the recess matched to it to prevent its turning.

The fence is drilled for wood screws ($1\frac{1}{4}$" #12 flathead used here) at $5\frac{1}{4}$ and $2\frac{1}{4}$" from its heel end, centered in the width covered by the bridle. With the fence aligned with the heel of the stock and just clearing the skate groove, and the bottom piece of the bridle aligned with the arm holes and in contact with

diameter of the holes made by the drill to be used for the bridle holes (a force fit), and must be uniform if the fence setting is to be smooth. I presume that this can be accomplished by an expert woodturner using

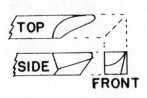

Figure 17:12

a skew in a wood lathe, or with a carefully set rounder. I chose to cut the arms in a metal lathe with a bit sharpened with very high rake (Fig. 17:12), using machine feed. Choose an end treatment to please yourself; I drilled and tapped the ends and mounted turned Teflon endpieces to create an appearance of ivory.

BRIDLE To ensure proper registration of the arm holes, both pieces of the bridle assembly are made in one piece. The blank is squared to $1\frac{5}{8}$ x $2\frac{1}{2}$ x $6\frac{1}{2}$", and centers for armholes are center-punched $1\frac{1}{2}$" from the bottom and $\frac{7}{8}$" in from each end. These are drilled in a press with a $\frac{3}{4}$" Forstner or other accurate drill bit. As smooth operation of the fence adjustment requires precise parallelism of the arms, care must be taken to ensure that the drill press the stock, mark for the screw pilot holes and drill them. The accuracy of the fence alignment depends on the placement of these. The hex head bolt is installed and the fence and bridle base screwed together. The upper portion of the bridle assembly is profiled on a band saw to please your eye, and filed and sanded smooth.

A thumb nut is made with a profile to complement the depth stop knob. It is drilled partly through from the bottom and tapped ($\frac{1}{4}$-20). The depth must permit accepting enough of the threaded end of the bolt buried in the bridle to allow tightening of the bridle on the arms. A washer to act as a bearing surface for this thumbnut is cut from brass plate, and inset into the top of the bridle.

The arms are glued into the holes in the body, the parts assembled, and you now have the pleasure of admiring the operation of your bridle.

WEDGE FITTING   Final adjustment of the wedge fit may now be made with paring chisel and floats, temporarily attaching the rear skate section for this purpose. The wooden wedge should contact both the iron and the front of the mortise over its full length, with the iron nesting exactly on the beveled front end of the rear skate. The fit is acceptable if a light tap on the wedge locks the iron in place. The area of the right side of the stock just in front of the lower wedge mortise was pared away to match the profile of the curve at the rear of the front skate. The lower end of the wedge is now cut off in a curve to continue this curve of the body. The wedge finial may be shaped to your preference; the one shown is Cauldwall's.

FINISH   The body is rounded at the top rear to provide a comfortable hand grasp, and chamfered to your taste. I continued to follow the Cauldwall model, using flat chamfers cut with a shoulder plane, met at toe and heel with matching vertical chamfers ending in a bevel cut, both done with a freshly honed chisel. After final surface preparation (scraping and sanding), the wooden parts may be finished as you please. I used a light mixture of water-soluble stains (yellow maple with a touch of red mahogany), after wetting, drying, and light sanding to remove raised grain. This was followed with a penetrating oil finish, and waxing. Metal parts were polished on a buffing wheel charged with an emery polishing bar.

Assemble the parts, sharpen the iron and try out your new tool.

MAKING A DEPTH STOP   The old planemakers did not make their hardware, but acquired it from the metal working trades. We cannot walk down the street to a local shop to order depth stops (as they did in early England), and therefore we must find another alternative. You may acquire a damaged plow, beyond repair but from which the depth stop may be cannibalized. You may find the assembly available from an antique tool dealer. Failing this, making a serviceable depth stop is well within the capability of the home shop. A common form of stop used in England and in early U.S. plows may be made with relatively little difficulty.

The foot of a plow depth stop is commonly made of steel $\frac{1}{8}$-$\frac{3}{16}$" thick, about 4" long and $\frac{3}{4}$-$\frac{7}{8}$" wide. The shape is seen in Fig. 17:13. One side of the center area of the foot is cut away for all but $\frac{3}{4}$" or so at each end. This cutout allows the foot to straddle the cutting iron, providing clearance for it and for the shavings, while the ends of the foot provide depth stop surfaces before and behind the cutting edge. These ends will be positioned to almost touch the skate of the plow.

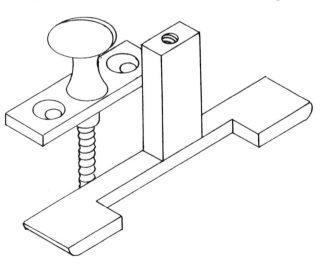

Figure 17:13

94

The narrow central section of the foot is mounted on the bottom of a shaft which slides in a mortise in the plow stock. This shaft is threaded to receive an adjustment screw. The screw passes through a bearing plate mounted on the top of the plow stock, is retained in it by a nut bearing on the under surface of the plate, and is equipped with a thumbscrew head.

Various designs are used for the vertical shaft of the depth stop. An iron shaft similar to the shaft of the dado stop of Fig. 15:10 is sometimes seen. A simple section of brass bar stock was a favorite of the early makers.

The attachment of the foot to the shaft was frequently effected by pinning. A steel pin was forced into the brass shaft and through a hole in the foot, peened over and filed flat. Close examination is required to see the outline of this pin on the bottom of the foot. Other stops show indications of assembly by brazing or soldering.

The procedure used to make the depth stop for the toted plow of Chapter 19 is outlined here, and the product is seen in Fig. 17:13. The dimensions given below are those used there, but may of course be changed to match available metal stock sizes and your prototype's dimensions.

The foot is cut from a four inch length of $\frac{3}{4}$ x $\frac{1}{4}$" brass strip. (As indicated in the dado chapter, I perversely prefer brass to steel, and slightly greater thickness than the conventional steel foot). A $2\frac{1}{4}$" long cutout in its center is made to provide clearance for the cutting iron, reducing the center section to the thickness of the shaft ($\frac{5}{16}$"). Its lower leading and trailing edges are filed round for smooth traverse of the workpiece.

The shaft starts as a $1\frac{1}{2}$" length of $\frac{5}{16}$ x $\frac{5}{8}$" brass bar stock with carefully squared ends. It is drilled lengthwise, starting with a centrally placed center punch mark, to within a half inch of the other end with a $\frac{1}{4}$" drill bit. This hole is met by one drilled from the other end with a #7 drill bit. These holes must be coaxial to accomodate the adjustment screw

without binding, and should be made in a drill press with the workpiece held precisely vertical in a drill press vise. (A machinist in a well-equipped shop will drill both holes from one end, the larger first. As the smaller hole must be centered, I prefer the less risky procedure above.) The smaller hole is threaded with a $\frac{1}{4}$-20 tap. If the holes fail to align and the adjustment screw binds, it is always possible to hacksaw a slot in the lower end of the shaft to clear the screw. (Fortunately this has never proved necessary with my stops.) The shaft and foot are silver soldered together (at the unthreaded end of the shaft). If you are unfamiliar with silver soldering, the classical method of pinning may be used. Conventional soldering is acceptable if the stronger silver-tin type of soft solder is used. Locate the shaft $1\frac{3}{8}$" back from the leading edge of the foot, after making sure that this placement satisfies your prototype.

The bearing plate is made from two inches of $\frac{5}{8}$" brass stock $\frac{3}{16}$ or $\frac{1}{4}$" thick, drilled $\frac{1}{4}$" at its center and drilled and countersunk for #10 mounting screws. The thumb knob is cut from $\frac{1}{2}$" brass stock, drilled partly through and tapped for the $\frac{1}{4}$" adjustment screw and filed to shape to match your prototype (a lathe is useful for turning the lower section). Alternatively, the knob may be lathe turned to your design (as shown in the sketch of the bridle plow stop in Fig. 17:6); or a brass casting may be acquired from one of the amateur brass casters located through one of the national tool organizations. A retaining nut is made from brass rod, drilled and threaded. A suitable (usually 2") length of $\frac{1}{4}$-20 threaded steel rod is screwed into the thumb knob and soldered or pinned in place. After removing visible solder, it is passed through the bearing plate and the retaining nut is screwed on, tight enough to avoid end play but allowing easy turning in the bearing. A small hole is drilled through nut and screw together, and a pin (a brad serves) driven through this hole keeps the nut in place.

CHAPTER 18

SCREW-ARMS AND THEIR FENCES

The two following chapters deal with screw-arm plow planes. As their arms and fences are very similar, the procedure for shaping them need only be covered once, here. The arm dimensions are based on use of a ¾" screwbox and tap, which are available from many woodworking supply houses. All dimensions given are, as always, subject to modification to the values of your prototype and tools.

A rounder set to cut the proper diameter should serve. If a metal lathe is available, rounding is accomplished with great accuracy using power feed, with a bit specially shaped for woodcutting (seen in Fig. 17:12) having a very high side rake angle.

The top of the shoulder is shaped into a semi-circular section with a block plane or a hollow plane, to continue the ¾" diameter of the arm. The lower part

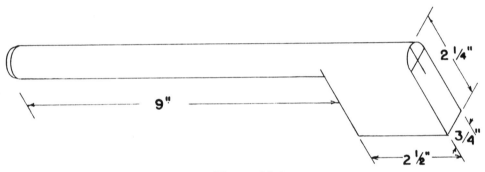

Figure 18:1

Two blanks for the two arms are prepared having nine inches of 1 x 1", and another 2½" inches of 1 x 2¼" for the shoulders. The 1 x 1" section is to be converted to a cylinder of ¾" diameter. Thinner stock, down to ¾", may be used, but there is a risk of leaving flat spots on the threads if the centers are not located precisely for converting the square section to round. Be sure that the arm length and the 2¼" height of the shoulder is adequate for your prototype.

The center point of the 1 x 1 is drilled for the dead center of the lathe, and a corresponding point is located at the shoulder end for the drive center. The arm is turned down to a uniform ¾" diameter up to the shoulder, with a short length at the end tapered down to ⅝" diameter to provide a smooth start for the screwbox. An expert touch with a skew chisel would be required to make the diameter uniform, and any deviation will be quite apparent after threading.

of the shoulder is planed to the finished width (¾"), to produce the form shown in Fig.18:1. The shoulder is clamped in a vise (suitably padded), and the screw threads are formed with a ¾" thread box (mine formed six threads per inch). A sharp cutter, properly set, makes quick work of this in applewood. Ebony is not much more difficult, but it dulled the cutter rapidly.

The common form of thread box cannot thread all of the way to the shoulder, as the entrance section of the box blocks the way. Having threaded as far as possible with the assembled box, it is removed from the work piece, and taken apart by removing the screws holding the two pieces together. The bare thread box is now threaded back onto the arm, taking care that the cutter enters the thread already cut. This allows continuation of the thread on the arm almost to the shoulder (now the screw holding the cutting iron blocks progress). The last few threads may be cut with a carver's veiner or similar V-chisel and a

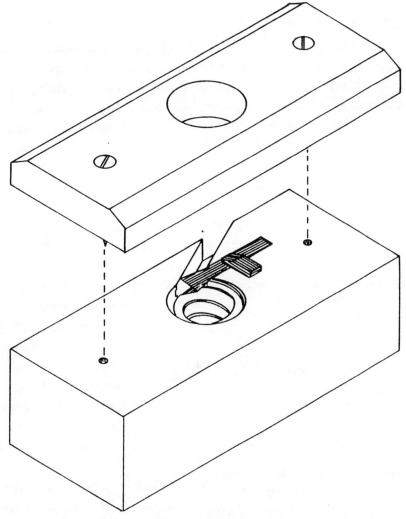

Figure 18:2

triangular file, after carefully marking them to match the others. (This problem was alleviated by the professional planemakers, who had screwboxes with the cutter held by a stirrup or an L-hook, as shown in Fig. 18:2.) An alternate procedure (used by many restorers but which I resisted the temptation to try) is to thread a dowel and turn down its end for insertion into a hole bored in a separate shoulder piece.

Each screw arm is adjusted and its position fixed in the stock by two wooden nuts screwed onto the arms. One is thin, threaded onto the shoulder side of the arm before it enters the stock; this is set to the proper spacing for the fence. It is sometimes, unfortunately, called the washer; the term "flat nut" seems more appropriate. The other nut, or "knob", bears on the other side of the stock and locks the arm in position.

The majority of old plows have nuts whose holes are aligned with the grain of the wood. Do not attempt to use this orientation in tapping your nuts with the presently available wood taps, which are shaped like large metal taps. These will break the threads during tapping, if used along the grain. Planemakers used a different type of tap, a hollow pipe threaded on the outside with the leading edge of the thread sharpened to a cutting edge. A hole behind this edge allowed the shaving to enter the interior of the pipe. Without this type of tap, the holes for the threads must be made across the grain, not with the grain of the wood.

The nuts and flat nuts are made from 2" stock, and their female threads are formed with the tap matching your thread box. Three clean $\frac{5}{8}$" holes are drilled (for the $\frac{3}{4}$" tap), leaving ample room for bandsawing 2" circles around the holes as center. Do not saw out these cylinders until the threads have been cut. Rather large torque is required for the tapping and straight-edge blocks are easier to hold firmly in your vise. A drill press helps in making the holes vertical, and again helps in making sure that the tap is properly aligned when starting the thread — the tap is chucked in the press and turned by hand until the thread is started. The block is then clamped in a sturdy vise to continue the threading. This requires rather more effort than cutting the male threads. Wax helps as a lubricant, and periodic withdrawal of the tap to clear shavings is necessary (as in metal threading). An allowance is provided in the 2" stock thickness to remove the ends marred by tap entry and exit.

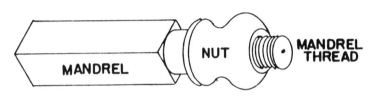

Figure 18:3

A simple mandrel is made to hold these members while turning their exteriors in the lathe. This is threaded in the same manner as the arms. After sawing the two-inch cylinders around the threaded holes, these are mounted (one at a time) on the mandrel, and trued. One is left cylindrical, and parted to form the two flat nuts, each ½" thick. The other two are turned into a profile that pleases you (the ones shown are copied from H. Chapin plows), to form the nuts. Fig. 18:3 shows a finished nut on the mandrel.

Arm end caps were made for the toted plow illustrated in the next chapter, from tagua nut (vegetable ivory), and these were epoxied in place. You may prefer another treatment. A cast plastic ivory substitute is now available, which allows larger end caps than I have been able to get from the nuts. For the ebony plow,

ivory ends were made (from fossil walrus ivory) by drilling mounting holes in ½" pieces, then turning these to cylindrical form. The arm ends were turned down to a diameter fitting the holes, and the caps epoxied in place.

Extra length has been allowed in the shoulder sections of the arm blanks to allow for removal of the marks of the lathe drive centers. Shaping the shoulders is deferred until the fence is completed.

FENCES　　The fences of screw-arm plow planes usually align with the heel of the stock but project forward of the toe by about an inch and a quarter (which helps in starting a cut with the plow). They are about three inches wide, and their height is at least a half inch greater then the distance from the bottom of the stock to the bottom of the skate. Square your stock to satisfy these dimensions. The top surface of the fence must have a pocket removed to permit the foot of the depth stop to reach full extension with the fence close to the stock. This is easier to cut if it is done before rabbeting the fence blank for molding. The position of this excavation may be located precisely on the fence blank if you have installed the depth stop in the plow body before starting the fence. Location and cutting of this pocket was described in the previous chapter, and sketched in Fig. 17:9; its

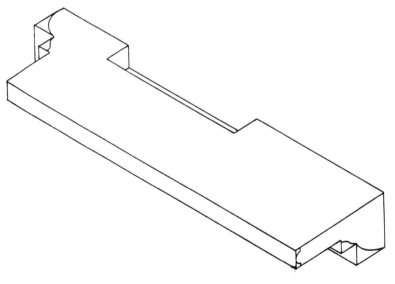

Figure 18:4

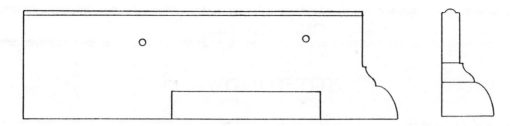

Figure 18:5

top outline is seen in 18:4.

Unless you wish to exactly duplicate your proto-type, simplifying the molding profile of its fence will save much effort. The professional had special planes (or, later, shaping machines) to cut these. You will have to work much harder than he did. Attractive profiles may be laid out which can be cut by molding planes available to you. This simplification was used for the applewood plow (Fig. 18:4), but not (to my regret) in the making of the ebony plow of Chapter 20.

Molding of a plow fence was described in the previous chapter; only a brief recap is given here. Lay out the desired molding profile, both on the rear and on the front top surface of the blank. Rabbet away the waste with right-angle cuts on the table saw, repeat-ing each cut on the front with the corresponding cut on the bottom of the fence. The fence at this point, for the toted plow of the next chapter, is seen in Fig. 18:4.

With the rabbets to guide your cuts, complete the moldings on the bottom of the fence. To avoid splin-tering on the end-grain cuts, it is safer to do these by nibbling with tablesaw or bandsaw, filing and sand-ing. Take pains to have the moldings meet in precise miters at the front corner. The finished fence is seen in Fig. 18:5.

ARMS (continued) With the arms inserted into their holes in the stock of the plow, mark their shoulders at the level of the bottom of the plow. Cut them off a mite ($\frac{1}{64}$") below this level, making sure

that the cut is parallel to the axis of the arms and at right angles to the sides of the shoulders. Thread the flat nuts onto the arms all the way to the shoulder, and insert the arms in their holes in the stock. Place the fence in its proper position under the sole of the stock, as close to the skate as allowed by the smallest plow iron. Scribe the position of the sides of the shoulders on the fence top. The arm shoulders will overhang the top of the fence. Mark the bottom of each arm shoulder with the location of the outermost end of the level top of the fence, where its molding starts. Scribe the shoulders with the same molding profile used on the fence, starting from this mark. The only change is required by the sharp arrises terminat-ing the fence moldings, the ones seen at the lower right of the isometric view of Fig. 18:4. These are rounded over at the top of the shoulders, as shown in Fig. 18:6. Form these shoulder moldings in the same manner as used for the front of the fence.

Drill the fence for the arm mounting screws, at the center of the shoulder locations just scribed on its top. Countersink these on the bottom of the fence, to accept the heads of the mounting screws (#12 or

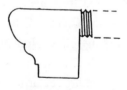

Figure 18:6

#14 x 1½" flathead wood screws). Mark the arm shoulders for pilot holes to match these, the shoul-ders positioned on their scribe marks. Drill these and assemble arms and fence.

CHAPTER 19

TOTED PLOW

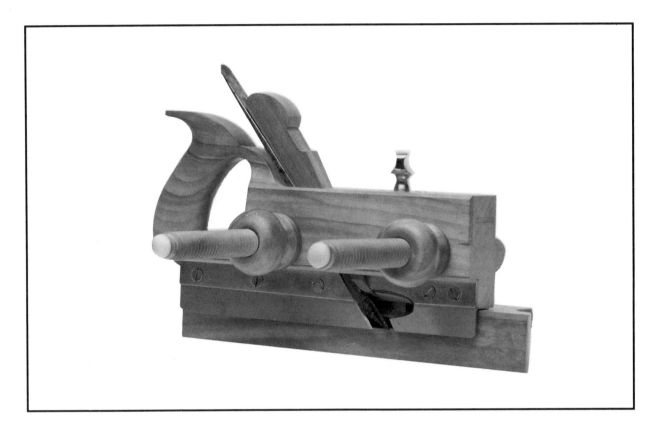

The applewood plow in the photograph was modeled after one made in the Union Factory under Hermon Chapin. This was described as a first-rate grooving plow, No.239, in the price list of 1859; its price, $6.25 with 8 irons. The good old days!

Making the arms, nuts and fences for this plow and the plow of the next chapter has been described in the previous chapter. Many of the remaining features are very similar to those described for the bridle plow of Chapter 17, so that only brief summaries and references are given here.

STOCK Our plow begins with a squared block $1\frac{3}{4}$ x 5 x $10\frac{1}{2}$", on which is laid out the pattern shown in Fig. 19:1. Waste wood is sawn away to expose the upper surface of the stock, three inches above the sole, and the rough outline of the upper tote profile. Take care that the flat section is cut parallel to the sole; a carefully adjusted bandsaw helps. Plane and scrape it flat.

Bedlines are marked on this upper surface of the stock $5\frac{1}{2}$" from the toe, and on the right side sloping forward at an angle of $52\frac{1}{2}°$ (a compromise between "York" and "middle" pitch used in the original). The outline of the wedge mortise is marked on the top, running forward from the bedline for a distance of $1\frac{1}{8}$", its right side $\frac{1}{4}$" from the right side of the stock and its width $\frac{5}{8}$". (One more reminder: the right side of any plane feature is on your right as you face the back of the plane.) The slope of the front of this mortise is made $8°$ steeper than the bedline, and is marked on the right side of the stock. You may prefer to mark bedlines on the left side of the stock as well as the right, for help in aligning the chisel cuts.

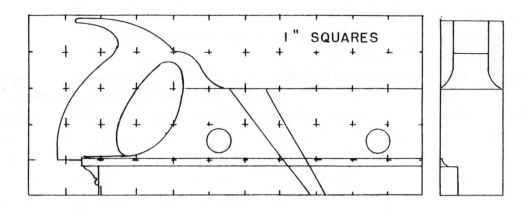

Figure 19:1

WEDGE MORTISE   The procedure for cutting the wedge mortise and fitting a wedge is the same for all of the plows considered here, and is given on p.89.

ARMHOLES   Holes are drilled in the stock to accept the screw arms. Their centers are located $4\frac{1}{2}$" apart, $1\frac{1}{2}$" below the top of the stock, with the forward one $1\frac{1}{4}$" from the toe. A $\frac{3}{4}$" drill bit is used, stopped just as the point breaks through to avoid splintering on exit; a Forstner bit is best. Complete by drilling from the other side, with careful centering on the point breakthrough. Unless a drill press is used to ensure that these holes are parallel and perpendicular to the stock side, they will probably have to be enlarged to attain smooth operation of the arms.

SKATE LOCATION   The bottom of the stock must be rabbeted to provide a mounting surface for the skate, the rabbet having a groove in its upper surface to house the top of the skate and sole plate. This operation has been described in detail on pp.89-90, so that a brief summary should serve here. A groove $\frac{3}{4}$" deep is cut in the sole, its width equal to the thickness of skate plus sole plate (0.158" for the present plane, as in the bridle plow). The groove is positioned to align the skate with the center of the wedge mortise. The right side of this groove is cut away to form a rabbet, leaving only $\frac{1}{8}$" of the groove remaining at the top of the rabbet. Because the tote prevents using the top of the stock as the guiding

surface against the rip fence, the bottom is used. This presents a hazard. The waste wood cut away is trapped between stock and rip fence; it can be caught by the blade and hurled backward with considerable force. Stand clear of the path of this potential projectile.

With the rabbet completed, its upper side is molded as you choose. A small ovolo molding plane serves well.

FITTING THE DEPTH STOP   Considerable time may be saved if you can acquire the hardware as such, or recover it from a damaged plow, either of which may sometimes be found at a flea market or in an antique tool dealer's stock. If you prefer to make your own, the procedure used for this plow was detailed at the end of Chapter 17, and the product is seen in Fig. 17:13. The thumbscrew head was hand filed to approximate that of the prototype.

Locate the foot of the depth stop to allow its cutaway section to clear the open area of the skate and the lower exit of your wedge mortise. The wider sections of the foot should almost touch the skate, and reach forward to within an inch of the toe of the stock. With the foot located, the position of the mortise to accept the upright shaft of the depth stop is determined. In the present case, the shaft was found to clear the wedge mortise by $\frac{1}{8}$", lying to the left and slightly in front of it. The position for the shaft mortise is transferred to the top of the stock and outlined there. The mortise is cut and pared to a

101

sliding fit for the shaft, without wobble. Recesses are cut to inlay the bearing plate of the depth stop in the top of the stock, and its foot in the bottom. This procedure is described in more detail on pp.94-95.

TOTE   The tote may now be shaped. The outline is completed on the bandsaw or with a turning saw. (If you have a maker's stamp, it is well to finish the toe and stamp your name on the front of the stock while you still have a solid support at the heel.) The hole in the tote is started by drilling through with appropriate drill bit sizes at top and bottom. A turning saw or coping saw completes the interior outline. The width of the tote must be reduced to one inch, and it is to be centered in the width of the stock. (Your prototype might be one of the plows whose tote is offset.) Careful use of a rip saw starts this process, which is completed by painstaking cuts with gouges and chisels.

The surfaces at front and rear of the handgrip should be shaped into semicircular or even elliptical profiles. These are roughed out with gouges, refined with rasps and files or perhaps with a drum sander (there is not too much opportunity for a spokeshave here), and finished with several grades of sandpaper. Appreciable time is required to attain a comfortable grip and an attractive appearance. The details at the bottom of the tote (sketched in Fig. 19:1) may now be shaped, echoing the molding profile used on fence front and arm shoulders and accomplished in the same way.

SKATE   The skate and sole plate are shaped and fitted as described on p.91, using the same materials. They are shown in Fig. 19:2. The stock of the plow behind the beveled front section of the skate is pared to continue the skate bevel, for shavings clearance, also as described there.

FENCE   The formation of the fence and arms has been covered in the previous chapter. Starting with a block squared to 3 x $1\frac{1}{2}$ x $10\frac{1}{2}$", a recess to clear the foot of the depth stop is laid out, following measurements taken from your installed depth stop. In the present case, it is sunk $\frac{3}{4}$" deep and wide, extending from $4\frac{1}{8}$ to $8\frac{1}{4}$" from the rear. An end mill does well; chisels would also serve.

The fence moldings are shown in Fig. 18:4. As these are simplified from the prototype, your choice of profiles will serve as well as the ones used for the plane illustrated. The process of cutting rabbets to locate the moldings, and the cutting procedure, is detailed on p.92. Making, molding and mounting the arms is described in the previous chapter.

FINISHING   The top arrises are lightly chamfered, and the chamfers continued down the front to terminate in gouge cuts $1\frac{1}{4}$" down from the top. Before mounting the metal parts, the wood may be finish scraped, sanded and coated. In keeping with the original model, I rubbed in several coats of boiled linseed oil. A light coat of wax on the screwarms, well buffed, facilitates setting. The metal parts were buffed with emery on a cloth wheel.

The skate sections are carefully positioned and mounted, using the procedure of pp.91-92. The depth stop is secured in place by screwing home its bearing plate. After threading the flat nuts on the arms up to the shoulders, pass the arms through the holes in the stock from the left side and screw on their nuts. Sharpen the iron, and try out your plow.

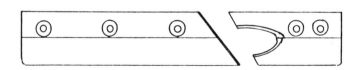

Figure 19:2

CHAPTER 20

EBONY PLOW

The gabon ebony plow seen in the photograph is a copy of the #244½ applewood plow, listed in H. Chapin's Son 1890 catalog at $6.50 (with eight irons). As the major details of construction are the same (except for the tote) as the applewood plow of the previous chapter, it is only necessary to spell out the differences arising from the different prototype, choice of wood and the choice of molding profile.

Ebony would be a poor choice for a first attempt at plane-making. Aside from being expensive and difficult to find in the proper size, the wood is hard and quite brittle. It planes beautifully with a very sharp iron and works well with a good chisel, but is hard on these edges. Time spent in sharpening your tools will save time (and temper) in the long run. Be prepared for a long clean-up. The black dust generated while working ebony will be quite visible for some time.

STOCK Dimensions of the stock are seen in dimensioned orthographic view in Fig.20:1. The stock is squared to 1⅞ x 3 x 8". The bedline is scribed on the side, from a point 2¼" from the heel on top of the stock down and forward at 50°. The line defining the front of the mortise starts at 1¼" forward of the bedline on top, and ends ⅝" forward at the bottom of the stock. Mortise outlines are continued across the top of the stock, and its sides are marked at ¼" and ⅞" from the right side. The bed angle is the same as used for the bridle plow, permitting the use of the same jig in the initial boring for the mortise. The mortise and wedge are completed as described on p.89. Sharp chisels find little difference between ebony and applewood while completing the wedge mortise, except for requiring more frequent honing with the former. Ebony's brittleness calls for even

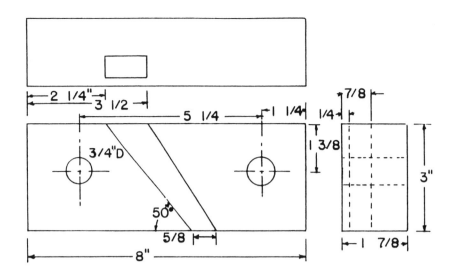

Figure 20:1

more than usual care to avoid splitting at the edges of the mortise.

The arm hole spacing in this plow is $5\frac{1}{4}$", the centers $1\frac{3}{8}$" down from the top and, for the front one, $1\frac{1}{4}$" from the toe. The armholes, and the groove and rabbet for the skate, are formed as described on pp.101 and 89-90.

SKATE The prototype has a deeper skate than the one used for the previous plow. It is matched by using steel stock a half inch wider ($\frac{3}{32}$ x 2") than the strip used there. The brass sole plates are $1\frac{3}{16}$" wide. The profile of the front skate section provides a less constricted oval for shavings escape. The shaping and mounting are described on pp. 91-92.

DEPTH STOP I was fortunate in acquiring at a tool auction a box of plane parts containing a depth stop mechanism from a Chapin plow. It was rehabilitated and used here. Little change was required in the procedure given on pp.90-91, in installing this in the stock. The steel foot easily cleared the wedge mortise, and came within $\frac{5}{8}$" of the toe.

ARMS AND NUTS The arm, nut and washer preparation follows the procedure outlined in Chapter 18. However, ebony's brittle nature causes problems, particularly in chipping at entry and exit while cutting the female threads. The stock used for the

nuts and flat nuts should allow a generous additional thickness, beyond that required for the length of the nuts, to allow cutting back to unchipped wood.

Another problem arises because ebony is rarely available as kiln dried stock. It is often received with a wax coating to avoid checking, and it is good practice to wax every new cut you make until the piece is ready for finishing. The nuts are subject to shrinkage as the wood dries, which tightens them on the arms. Let them come to equilibrium, checking them for fit every day or so for a month before installing them permanently on the arms. They may be difficult to remove otherwise. Tight nuts should be retapped with the original tap (you will be surprised at how much wood this removes). In the present case, retapping was done after several months of low humidity, in the winter. It would be wise to wait for this time of year before tapping your fittings again. Mine have remained smoothly adjustable since their retapping.

Retapping after the nuts have been turned to final shape risks chipping at the tap exit. The plane illustrated had a sizeable chip returned to one nut, glued in place with cyanoacrylate adhesive. (Wash the area to be glued with lacquer thinner or other strong solvent before gluing.) I would recommend that the extra length used while first tapping the nuts be retained during the turning, and that the nuts be

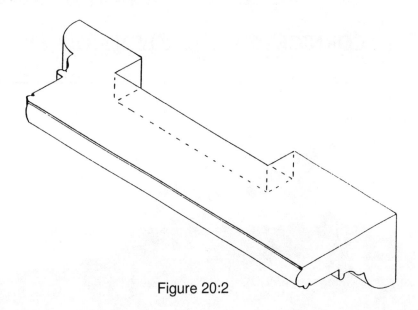

Figure 20:2

allowed to age in this shape until you feel they have stabilized. They can then be retapped as needed, and any chipping will be removed when they are cut to length. (I'm not sure I would have had this much patience!) Checking or chips may be repaired with a filler made from ebony sawdust and a two-part epoxy cement.

FENCE   The fence block was cut to $9\frac{1}{4}$ x 3 x $1\frac{3}{4}$", and finished as sketched in Fig. 20:2 (or with molding profiles of your prototype or choice). In making the plow of the last chapter, I simplified the molding profiles used in the prototype. As they are purely decorative and can require considerable effort if too ornate, it seemed unnecessary for a working tool. The professional planemakers used a special set of tools to stick these profiles. They cannot be cut with conventional molding planes, unless these are modified to deal with interferences. Using their tools, the additional effort is insignificant. Without them it is not.

For this plane, I attempted to duplicate the molding profiles of the model. I do not recommend this unless you have great patience and are willing to use it in creating an exact reproduction of your prototype (or are willing to make the special molding planes).

You will note that the same profile is repeated on the front and sides of the fence, and on the arm shoulders. The same set of special planes served the planemakers for all three.

After removing the recess for the depth stop (p.92), the molding profile copied from the prototype is scribed on the top front and the heel of the fence blank, and on the arm shoulders. The waste is rabbeted away, and the end-grain profiles are nibbled out with a band-saw, leaving a comfortable margin for finishing. The end grain patterns should be refined with smooth files, as rasps may cause splintering of the edges. The bottom of the fence may be nibbled away with a rabbet or plow plane to approximate the profile, and profiling continued with hollows and rounds. There are areas inaccessible to these which must be finished with carving tools, rasps, and files, followed by scraping with specially cut blades in a scratch stock. This procedure can consume several days. The product is seen in Fig. 20:2.

Finishing touches include the usual rounding of the top of the heel for a comfortable grip, and chamfering. Ebony is content with just a few coats of a good furniture wax well buffed (skipping the gripping surfaces of the wedge and mortise). If you prefer, two coats of tung oil may precede this.

105

CHAPTER 21

CORNICE PLANE (CROWN MOLDER)

You will often hear almost any wide molding plane, especially those with bench type throats, called a crown molder. In fact, many of these were not intended for crown or cornice moldings; there were many other locations in interior architecture calling for wide moldings.

The names crown and cornice came originally from ancient Greek architecture, and were borrowed and Anglicized as this style became popular in the early 19th century. Technically, the crown (corona) is the topmost section of the cornice, which is a series of moldings at the top of a significant part of a structure. As moldings became less ornate, the crown and cornice merged into one pattern. The late 19th century planemakers' catalogs invariably listed the planes made to cut these as "cornice" planes. The name "crown" appeared in later millwork listings. Any definite statement on how these planes were

used is reasonably certain to evoke differences of opinion. However named or used, these are impressive tools and highly valued by collectors.

Cornice (or crown) moldings were commonly used as a decorative feature where interior walls and ceilings met, providing a slanting transition between them. Rather than using thick stock for these angled moldings, they were cut on lumber only thick enough to accomodate the profile. These thinner moldings were then mounted at an angle, usually 45°. Their profiles reflect this. The V cut in the center of the molding made by the plane illustrated becomes a horizontal and a vertical fillet when so mounted.

Similar crowns or cornices used as finishing decorations on the top of furniture pieces were built up of several smaller moldings, as cutting the complete profile at once in hardwood was impractical. You have only to use one of these wide planes on soft

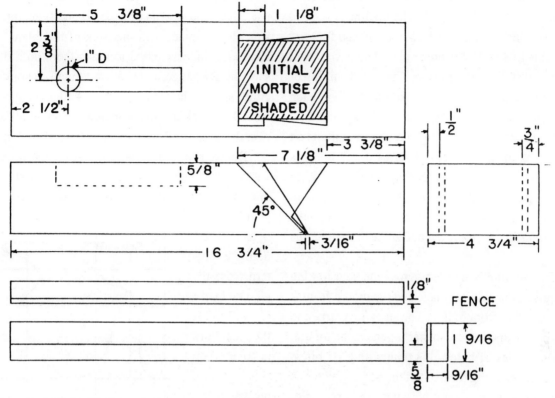

Figure 21:1

pine to agree with this. The architectural cornice was cut in straight-grained softwood, usually roughed out with hollows, rounds and rabbets or V-planes and finished with the wide molder. These finishing molders include the widest wooden planes known.

The availability of a large block of applewood (which squared to 16¾ x 4¾ x 3") seemed to demand the making of a crown molder. Although there were several deep checks, these were not structurally troublesome. The wood had been air dried for many years, and was regarded as stable enough to tolerate sealing these. They were filled with epoxy.

In contrast to the sequence used with most of the molders treated earlier, it was decided to open the throat in the classical manner, that is, prior to molding the sole. The advantage of having a stable flat bottom, and the protection against damaging a finished profile during the vigorous chisel work on the large throat, outweigh the problems to be faced in profiling.

The prototype chosen for the body style is a plane by Mockridge & Francis (Newark, NJ, 1835-68), a cabinet ogee with a 4" iron. It is unusual in that it has a closed tote; almost all molding planes this wide use an open tote. The sole profile is to be changed to the usual cornice double ogee form, and a slightly narrower blade is necessary. In addition, I chose to use a somewhat more difficult throat opening (one I have very seldom seen in a western molding plane, and never in a cornice plane). Most professionally made molders (except for the Japanese) do not have a uniform mouth opening in front of the blade. The higher points of the profiled cutting edge of the iron have a wider mouth opening before them than do the lower points, because the slope of the lower throat front is steeper than that of the bed. The sequence to be described is designed to keep this opening uniform. The advantage gained in use is marginal, and you may prefer to use the classical sequence of opening the mouth fully while the sole is still flat, before profiling.

107

Dimensioned views of the stock and attached fence are given in Fig. 21:1. The bedline is scribed on top of the block at $7\frac{1}{8}$" from the toe, and forward from this line at 45° on both sides. The throat front is marked at $3\frac{3}{8}$" from the toe. The initial sinking of the throat retains a cheek thickness of $\frac{3}{4}$" on each side. The block is supported at a 45° angle in a jig similar to that shown in Fig. 12:8 (with battens on both sides of the jig), and a series of $\frac{1}{4}$" holes is drilled from the top, just clearing the bedline. With these as guides, a mortise chisel clears the throat to within $\frac{3}{4}$" of the sole. The throat front is cut to make a plane surface meeting the bed at the bottom of this cut.

The bedline is marked across the sole joining the ends of the side bedlines, and the mouth front is marked $\frac{3}{16}$" in front of this. The stock is returned to the jig, sole and toe up, to start opening the mouth. Another series of holes, this time with a $\frac{1}{8}$" bit, is drilled just clearing the front of the bed surface. The jig makes these register nicely with the first series of holes, and they provide a useful guide in paring the bottom of the bed. The mouth is cleared with a compass saw (the Japanese type works well). For the present, the lower throat front is left parallel to the bed plane, $\frac{3}{16}$" away from it, to allow ample room for adjustment of the mouth clearance.

The abutment line is drawn on top of the stock 1 $\frac{1}{8}$" in front of the bedline, and extended down the sides to the front of the mouth on the sole. The abutments extend $\frac{1}{4}$" toward each side (leaving $\frac{1}{2}$" of cheek). The bed surface is extended outward with the compass saw, and another pair of sawcuts is made for the abutments (it is permissible to enlarge the lower throat opening at each side, just enough to provide access for the saw). The waste between these cuts is cleared with chisels. (The more detailed description of the cutting of a throat in Chapter 6 might be reviewed to seek more information on these steps.)

An iron blank 8 x $3\frac{3}{4}$" is hacksawed from four inch $\frac{3}{16}$" thick flat ground stock of soft tool steel. (I hope that you find a stock blank wide enough to take the full four inches.) The bed surface of the plane,

which at this stage remains roughly cut by the mortise chisel and saw, is now pared and floated to ensure close contact with the back of this blank. The abutment slots are pared to make them both fit the same wedge gauge, and to allow a small clearance on either side of the iron. (A set of wedge gauges, cut from $\frac{3}{16}$" stock at angles increasing in small steps over the range 7-12 degrees, is well worth making.)

Before proceeding with the sole profiling, advantage is taken of the stable bottom to sink the mortise for the tote. The closed tote is made from stock a bit over 1" thick, using a pattern from the prototype (Fig. 21:2); the procedure is covered on p. 37. The mortise is begun with a 1" hole centered in the width and $2\frac{1}{2}$" from

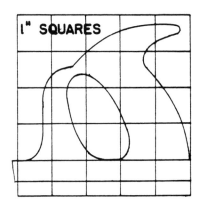

Figure 21:2

the heel, drilled $\frac{5}{8}$" deep in the top of the stock. An end mill, followed by squaring the forward end with a chisel, extends it forward for a total length of $5\frac{3}{8}$" and a depth of $\frac{5}{8}$". (Chisels and a hand router also serve.) The tote is fitted into this, but not installed as yet.

The prototype has an applied fence, and this is duplicated here. A blank matching the length of the stock and $1\frac{9}{16}$ x $\frac{9}{16}$" in section has a rabbet $1\frac{5}{16}$ x $\frac{1}{8}$" removed. The top is coved with a round plane. It is shown in Fig. 21:1 and its profile and position are shown in the heel view of the finished stock (Fig. 21:3). Three holes for 1"-#11 screws are drilled and countersunk $\frac{1}{2}$" from the top of the fence. Delay drilling the corresponding pilot holes in the left side of the stock and mounting the fence until the sole has been profiled.

The development of the profile is shown in Fig. 21:4. Scribing the final form on heel and toe of the

108

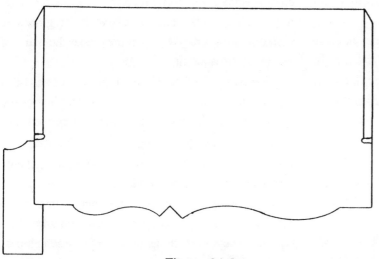

Figure 21:3

the profile. This produces the middle diagram in 21:4.

The convex sections of the two ogees are then roughed out with hollow planes, cutting arcs joining smoothly with the cove cuts and the 45° cuts at the sides of the stock. Scraper blades are ground to the profile of each of the ogees, and the profile is finished with these. The product is seen in the bottom sketch of 21:4. There must be no deviation from a straight line in the path of the scrapers from toe to heel. It is very important that a straightedge laid from toe to heel at any point on the profile is in contact with it over its full length.

stock beforehand is insurance against a wrong cut (which would be heartbreaking at this stage!). It is begun with a pair of 45° table saw cuts meeting $1\frac{7}{8}$" from the left side of the sole at a depth of cut of $\frac{3}{16}$". Two more 45° degree cuts are made to the same depth, to meet the two horizontal lines marking the depth stops, at $\frac{1}{2}$" from the sides. These serve as references lines for the generation of the ogees of the profile. The horizontal cuts for the depth stops which meet these angle cuts are delayed until after the coves are cut, in the next step. The sketch at the top of Fig.21:4 shows the heel view at this point.

The hollows of the two ogees are roughed out by cove cuts on the table saw (as detailed on p.62). The wider one to the right side of the notch is laid out to meet the center notch at its right bottom, and to extend right for $1\frac{1}{4}$". The depth of cut is made $\frac{11}{64}$". The set-up is carefully checked on scrap stock before making these cove cuts.

The second cove cut to the left of the notch is set up to slightly overcut into the notch wall and to have a width of $\frac{11}{16}$", with the same depth of cut.

After making these coves, the horizontal cuts for the depth stops are made on each side, making sure that they are slightly higher than the deepest points of

With the sole completed, the next crucial step is shaping the iron to match it. The wedge should be available at this point to hold the blade firmly while scribing. A blank 1 x $3\frac{3}{4}$ x 8" is cut to the required wedge angle, carefully fitted, and shaped as described on pp.33-34.

A coat of machinist's layout dye on the bottom front of the blade blank helps to make scribe marks visible. The blank is wedged firmly in place, with its lower end just below the lowest point of the sole profile. The profile is transferred to the front of the blank with a scriber. Because the mouth front is still narrow at this point, almost touching the front of the

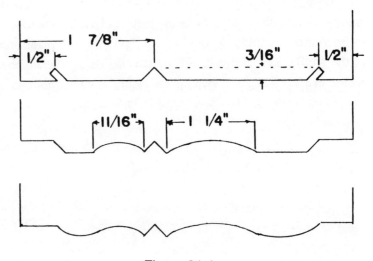

Figure 21:4

109

blank, it is possible to do this accurately. Care at this point saves much effort later.

In earlier chapters, molders with wider mouths had the rear of their blades scribed, and the profile cut at right angles to the face. Having an accurate profile at the front of the iron permits profiling at the desired bevel angle (25°) from the start. (In this case particularly, this saves much additional grinding and filing. I suspect that even the molders with wider mouths were scribed on their front by professional makers.) Leave the cutting edge blunt until after heat treatment. The iron profile is roughed out with a hacksaw, continued with a coarse grinding wheel, and finished with files. The match to the sole should be as close as you can make it at this point; corrections are more difficult after hardening. Check repeatedly by wedging the iron in place and sighting along the sole.

The iron is too large to attempt hardening it with equipment available in the usual home shop. A local machine shop provided this service for me (my thanks to K.H. Neuweiler, Inc. for their courtesy). The face of the iron is flattened on a coarse water stone, and smoothed with diamond hones. The bevel is sharpened with small stones in a hand grinder, with frequent checks to ensure that the match to the sole profile is not changed, and honed with slip stones.

With the iron finished, the lower throat of the plane is opened with small chisels, gouges and files. The objective is to provide a widening channel for the shavings as they move up the face of the iron, while maintaining a uniform mouth opening of $\frac{1}{16}$" in front of the cutting edge over the ups and downs of the profile. This clearance errs on the small side rather than making the opening too wide; it can always be enlarged. The lower throat front after this process echoes the profile for a short distance, but the slopes of these cuts is chosen to have the irregularities even out into a straight line as they meet the plane of the upper throat front.

Widening the front of the upper throat has been deferred until this step is completed. The line of the throat front on the top of the stock is extended outward to within $\frac{3}{8}$" of the sides of the stock. A compass or similar saw is used to make diagonal cuts extending the throat front, along this line on the top but not cutting into the abutment ears at their lower end. The wedge-shaped waste is removed with chisels, and the eyes are cut as in previous bench planes.

The top rear of the stock is eased with a piloted corner rounding bit in a power router, and shallow chamfers are cut on the top side arrises. Gouge cuts are made in the front and rear arrises to stop their chamfers at the level of the top of the applied fence, and these chamfers are cut with a chisel. After final cleaning of stock and fence with a scraper and sandpaper, the applied fence is screwed into position and the tote is glued in place. Moisture-cure urethane was used for my plane. (A better choice might have been yellow glue, as the foaming characteristic of the former material caused some extrusion from the mortise and a bit of a cleanup problem.) My name stamp was embossed on the front of the stock and the year (1995) stamped on the heel. Four coats of tung oil thinned with turpentine finished the stock photographed.

The final test, as always, is the performance of the tool. After repeated trials and profile refining, the plane shown produced a satisfactory cut on straight grain pine that had been roughed out with table saw, hollows, rounds, and a rabbet.

CHAPTER 22

SPOKESHAVE

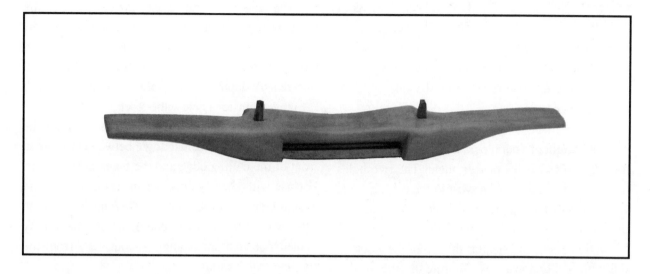

The spokeshave is far more versatile than its name indicates, being the instrument of choice in most cases for shaping doubly curved surfaces. Many people consider the wooden versions more pleasant to use than the metal varieties, because of their different blade configuration and warmer feel.

IRON   The cutting iron should be in hand before starting to make this tool. It is sketched in Fig.22:1. These irons are still being made in small quantities in England (Bristol Design). Old ones may be acquired from an antique tool dealer, or found at flea markets (perhaps in the form of a damaged spokeshave). Avoid the pitted ones. The cutting surface will warp when the iron is installed if the tangs are not truly parallel to each other. They must be made so (without bending the cutting section) before layout. Unless you are an accomplished blacksmith or have access to one, starting from scratch to make your cutting iron would be a major challenge.

The cutting edge is made with a bevel only on its upper surface, between the tangs. The under side, like the face of a plane blade, should be kept flat. The bevel is honed with a stone or slip small enough to fit between the tangs.

The iron used in the tool photographed has a 4" edge, with tangs $\frac{7}{32}$" across flats. These extend out from the sides of the blade, then turn upward and taper slightly toward their tops. These sections are at right angles to the edge when viewed edge on, but slant slightly forward from the plane of the cutting section as seen from the side, making an angle of about 83°.

LAYOUT   The spokeshave starts as a squared block of boxwood 11 x $1\frac{3}{8}$ x $\frac{7}{8}$". Beech or another fine-grained hardwood may be substituted, but the premium tools were made of boxwood for its greater split resistance. The tight

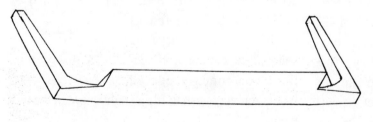

Figure 22:1

111

fit of the tangs in their holes puts much stress on the wood.

The location of these holes is laid out first. Accuracy in the spacing between holes, to match the spacing of the tangs of your blade, is essential to proper fit. Their centers are marked at equal distances from the ends of the stock. The wide section of the iron, between the tangs, is to be centered in the width of the stock. This places the hole centers toward the rear (in the present tool, $\frac{1}{2}$" from the side opposite the cutting edge).

As the plane of the cutter should match the present bottom of your block, the holes for the tangs must be drilled at the proper angle. The two holes must be parallel to avoid a twist in the cutting edge. Cut a wedge of scrap to the angle complementary to the one between your tangs and their cutting plane (7° in this case), and support the top of the stock on this while drilling in a press. Be sure that the slope is in the right direction. A drill size is chosen very slightly larger than the flat-to-flat dimension of your upright tang sections at their center.

FITTING THE IRON   These holes are than squared with a square needle file, proceeding carefully with frequent checking for fit. The fit must be very tight to hold the blade immobile during use, requiring mallet blows to seat it. Do not overdo the tightness in the direction across the grain of the stock; the other direction is more resistant to splitting. Finish with the horizontal tang extensions (which connect the cutting section to the vertical tangs) touching the stock. Scribe their outlines, to mark the edges of the recess which will be inlet for them later. Mark the location of the cutting edge on the bottom of the block.

Remove the iron, tapping alternately on the tops of the tangs. Draw lines, at right angles to the sides, across the bottom and rear of the block at the locations of the ends of the cutting section. Using a fine backsaw, make angled cuts on these two pairs of lines, terminating just before the location of the cutting edge on the bottom, and $\frac{1}{8}$" down from the top of the stock at the rear. Remove the waste between

these cuts with chisels, paring to a smooth surface. This provides the angled throat for shavings escape. A cross section through the middle of the finished tool (Fig. 22:2) shows the center profile after this operation.

The tang extensions must now be inlet into the stock. Using a small chisel, sink the outlines of their sides (which were marked as described earlier). Deepen these and remove waste between them until they reach a depth slightly more than required to sink the tang extensions below the stock surface.

The sole of the spokeshave body should now be modified to create a small angle between the sole in front of the cutting edge and the plane of the cutter. For use with sharply concave surfaces, this section should be curved. For general use (and if it is to be fitted with a brass wear plate), it may be simply planed flat at a small angle (about 10°) from the former stock bottom.

BRASS SOLE   If you choose to add a brass sole to your tool (without it the wooden sole will wear very rapidly), this is now cut from brass plate. Its length equals that of the cutting edge and the width is slightly more than the distance from cutting edge to the front of the stock. It is drilled and countersunk for two screws to hold it in position. The portion of the wooden sole in front of the cutting edge is recessed to receive this plate, and it is screwed in position. Be sure the screwheads do not project above the brass surface. The edge of the brass in front of the cutting edge is filed to a bevel matching the bevel of the wooden throat, allowing just a small horizontal distance between brass and cutting edge when the iron is driven into place. The shaded section of Fig.22:2 represents this brass sole, in front of the solid black cutting iron section. For concave curved

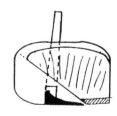

Figure 22:2

work, you may wish to file a slight curve in the wear plate.

112

SHAPING   The stock may now be shaped to your preference. A close copy of an authentic spokeshave is recommended, such as is seen in Fig. 22:3. This shape has survived for more than three centuries, and is a comfortable one to use. Having marked both vertical and horizontal profiles on the stock, the vertical profile is bandsawn first, then (with the stock resting on its top) the horizontal. The further shaping may be accomplished with your choice of tools; I used a spokeshave, cabinetmaker's rasp and files followed by drum sanders and hand sanding. Several coats of boiled linseed oil followed by buffed wax is a good finish.

The blade is then seated with mallet blows. Some final fitting with the needle file may be needed, but do not overdo this. The final fit must be tight enough to keep the blade from shifting in use. The vertical spacing between the cutting edge and the brass plate is set to the shaving thickness desired. This may be set, if you prefer, to allow one end of the blade to take a slightly thicker shaving than the other (for roughing and finish cuts). The shave may be used in either direction (pushed or pulled), switching as required by the changing grain direction in the curved workpiece.

If the tang fit is not tight enough to hold your blade setting under vigorous use, a remedy is available. This is often seen in old spokeshaves whose irons loosened after long use. A slip of wood shaving is inserted into each tang hole (against the end grain of the tang hole) before replacing the iron.

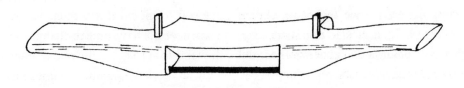

Figure 22:3

113

CHAPTER 23

MAKING PLANE IRONS

Plane irons recovered from damaged planes, which are frequently available from antique tool dealers or at various tool meets, offer the simplest source. Only those which are free from pitting are useful.

Authentic irons were made by forge welding together long strips of steel and wrought iron, then cutting or punching the product into blanks. The line of union of the wrought iron (the shank end, if a molding iron) and the steel is usually visible. There must be enough steel remaining to permit shaping the profile you need.

If you wish to make your own, there are two options. To copy the early style requires a skilled blacksmith, as forge welding steel to iron is not easy. If you have this skill, or know someone who has, and a source of wrought iron, a realistic reproduction can be made. If your interest is in a tool for use rather than an accurate reproduction, it is much easier to use tool steel throughout. In either case, the hardening and tempering procedures are similar.

STEEL   The steel is obtainable from machine shop mill supply sources, either local or through mail order. It is usually listed as "ground flat stock" and is available in many grades and sizes. The steel should be annealed ("dead soft") as supplied, but this is a usual form. Either the water hardening type (such as W-1) or oil hardening (O-1) will serve; there is no need to use high speed steel, which requires hardening conditions more difficult to attain. The irons described here were made with O-1 of $\frac{1}{8}$" thickness for small bench planes or molders, or thicker for the wider planes ($\frac{3}{16}$" for the cornice plane).

The procedure for shaping a required iron is given with several of the individual plane treatments in earlier chapters. The shaped plane iron must be hardened and tempered if it is to hold a useful cutting edge. It is hardened by heating to redness and quenching. Properly done, the steel is then glass hard, but it is too brittle to stand up in use. It is tempered by heat treatment to produce a useful balance between hardness and toughness.

TECHNICAL DIGRESSION   A brief and oversimplified explanation of the reasons behind the processes may help. Steel can exist in two crystalline forms, the soft form which is stable at room temperature, and the hard form into which it is converted above a certain transition temperature. If the hot hard form is allowed to cool slowly, it transforms back to the soft form; but if it is quenched rapidly, the hard form does not have time to change over, and remains. It wants to soften, but the rate of transformation is so slow at room temperature that it remains unchanged for centuries. As the temperature is increased, however, the change from hard to soft speeds up. By increasing the temperature carefully, the rate of change is controlled; only part of the hard form changes, so that a desired degree of toughening is attainable. Accurate control of temper is best done in a thermostatically controlled oven, but the old-fashioned method of judging temper by oxidation colors will give acceptable results.

As iron is heated, its surface combines with the oxygen of the air to form a thin, colored film of oxide. The color has no direct relationship with the hardness of the steel (even mild steel, which cannot be hardened, will show these colors). Color does, however, indicate the temperature that the steel has reached, which controls the rate of softening. By watching the color development, tempering may be stopped at the desired point.

Although this process may seem rather intimidating at first appearance, it is not difficult. Factories now use elaborate furnaces and temperature controls, but centuries ago useful irons were made by the simple process outlined here. To get a feel for the procedure and gain confidence in it before applying it to an iron you have painstakingly shaped, it is well to practice with a piece of the steel you will be using.

HARDENING   If you are not sure of the degree of red heat required to harden steel, a simple test is available. If the temperature is high enough to convert the steel to its hard form, a magnet will not be attracted to the hot area. Once you have succeeded in hardening a sample, you will be able to recognize the color required and will not need the magnet.

A plane iron is hardened by heating to this degree of redness for a brief period, followed by quenching. Only the lower section, the business end near the cutting edge, need be hardened. (In fact, it is preferable for the tang of a molding plane iron to be left soft.) If a forge is not available, a large natural gas burner or several hand propane torches used together provide enough heat for all but large irons. When full red is reached (a distinct red glow when seen in subdued light) and held for a few seconds, the iron is plunged vertically into water and stirred briskly. (Water serves, but brine and oil both have advocates.)

The cooled plane iron should now be hard enough to scratch glass. A file will not cut it (don't use a good file for the test). If these tests are not met, it will be necessary to repeat the hardening operation. Fully hardened steel is too brittle for use, but must be tempered to give the needed toughness (at the cost of some hardness).

TEMPERING   The hardened area of the iron is polished to brightness with emery paper. It is carefully heated in a low flame of a propane torch directed well away from the cutting edge (a much more reliable procedure is to lay the plane iron on a sheet of metal which is then heated from below). As the temperature of the iron increases, oxidation colors begin to appear, first in the hottest area and moving toward the cooler. The first pale straw color should move slowly and uniformly toward the cutting edge. If it moves rapidly or does not promise to reach all areas of the profile nearly simultaneously, quench, repolish, and try again with adjustment of the heating rate. The straw color is followed by progressively darker yellow-browns and then blue. The iron must be quenched in water before the blue reaches the cutting edge, or it will not be able to stay sharp. (You can polish away the blue color and repeat the development of the tempering colors, but this will do no good; the damage has been done.) You undoubtedly remember the blue color that appeared so quickly on the edge when you first attempted to sharpen a chisel on a grinding wheel, and your failure to get a good edge thereafter.

Control the hardness desired by the color allowed to develop at the cutting edge. Bench plane blades should be quenched as soon as the light straw color reaches the edge. Molding plane irons, which you will wish to refine and sharpen with files, may be allowed to develop a deeper brown before quenching.

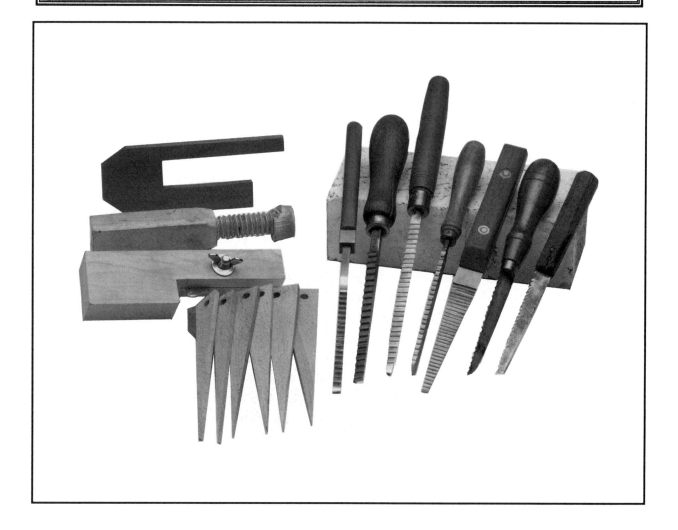

Wooden planes have been made for a wide range of purposes, in a great variety of forms. Even attempting to catalog and describe all of the planes that have been made would call for an enormous volume (and several lifetimes). The twenty planes chosen for treatment here are only a small sample of the many planes that have been made in large numbers and offered commercially. We have, however, examined enough types to have considered the individual steps required to make almost any of them. Choose any plane that you would like to duplicate, and it is likely that you will find enough information here to assist you.

The descriptions have been written with the intent of making them complete enough to allow duplication of the planes treated. I hope, however, that you do not follow the directions too closely. They record what was done in my shop, with the equipment that I had to hand, catering to my inclination of the moment; and they work. However, your shop and equipment will be different, as will your preferred methods of working. Get a prototype, a plane you would like to make. Duplicate it with the tools you have, in the way you wish to proceed. You will be in closer touch with the original, pre-professional, makers of planes; they adapted their everyday working tools to the making of the planes they needed. Make some of the tools they made to assist them. Shown in the above photograph are (top) scratch stock, mandrel for plow nuts, bedding gauge, with wedge gauges below; on the right, floats and planemaker's saws.

The photograph below shows a few of the planes my workshop has produced over the years. Most of these are reproductions of tools of historical signifi-cance. Making them, and the planes described herein, has given me much pleasure. I wish you the same!

APPENDIX: CALCULATING THE ANGLES FOR SKEW MORTISES

The equations below may seem intimidating if you haven't used trigonometry for a while, but an inexpensive scientific hand calculator (one which includes the trigonometric functions and their inverse functions) solves them painlessly.

The skew angle is defined as the angle between the bedline on top of the stock and the front (or back) of the stock. The bed angle is measured between the bedline on the side of the stock, and the sole. The blade angle is defined as the angle between the cutting edge and the side of the iron (the one less than 90°). These are shown in the sketch. Then the sine of the skew angle is equal to the cosine of the measured blade angle divided by the cosine of the bed angle you have chosen. This can be worked backward to calculate the required blade angle from the measured skew and bed angle. Cosine of bed angle times sine of skew angle gives the cosine of the blade angle.

For cutting the bedline, the required tilt angle for the table saw blade may be calculated. The tangent of the tilt angle is equal to the cosine of the skew angle divided by the tangent of the bed angle.

The angle between back and sides of the wedge differs from a right angle; the difference may be called the wedge skew. (It is the complement of the angle between the back of the wedge and its side). The tangent of the wedge skew is equal to the tangent of the skew angle times the sine of the bed angle.

The wedge skew angle between the FRONT of the wedge and the side, in a side escapement type wedge, is calculated in the same way using, in place of the bed angle, the angle between the layout line for the front of the wedge mortise and the sole of the stock.

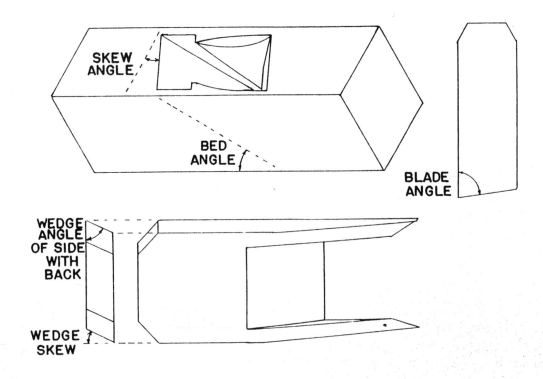

BIBLIOGRAPHY and Related Reading

Barker, Dwight, "Reproducing an Antique Plow Plane"; Fine Woodworking, July 1991, pp. 68-70, Taunton Press, Newtown, CT

Beck, Grant, "Milling and Drilling Machinist Style"; Fine Woodworking Vol.81, Dec. 1993, pp. 74-76, Taunton Press, Newtown, CT

Bertorelli, Paul, "The Woodworker's Tools"; Fine Woodworking, May 1984, Taunton Press, Newtown, CT

Blackburn, Graham, "Old Wooden Planes"; Fine Woodworking, March 1986, Taunton Press, Newtown, CT

Bourdeau, Robert, "A Pair of Panel-Raising Planes"; Fine Woodworking, Sept. 1981, p. 59, Taunton Press, Newtown, CT

Dittmer, Karl, "Making a Modern Wooden Plane"; Fine Woodworking, Jan.1975, p. 65, Taunton Press, Newtown, CT

Dolan, Charles, "Making the Iron"; Fine Woodworking, Nov. 1985, p.63, Taunton Press, CT

Dunbar, Michael, *Antique Woodworking Tools,* 1977, Hastings House, New York

Dunbar, Michael, *Restoring, Tuning and Using Classic Woodworking Tools,* 1989, Sterling Pub lishing, New York

During, Stefan, "Mortising the Throat in Wooden Planes"; Fine Woodworking, Jan. 1986, p.10, Taunton Press, CT

Ellsworth, Timothy (1975), "Hand Planes"; Fine Woodworking, Winter 1975, p. 22, Taunton Press, CT

Gentry, George, *Hardening and Tempering Engineer's Tools,* 1977, Argus Books Ltd., Hertfordshire, England

Goodman, W.L. (1993), *British Planemakers from 1800*, Third Edition (see Rees); The Astragal Press

Hoadley, Bruce (1980), *Understanding Wood;* Taunton Press, CT

Kahn, Donald, "Making Wooden Planes with Hand Tools"; The Toolshed, Sept.1993, pp. 6-7; CRAFTS of NJ, Murray Hill, NJ

Kahn, Donald, "The Planemaker's Float", The Toolshed, Apr.1994, p. 9; CRAFTS of NJ, Murray Hill, NJ

Kingshott, Jim, *Making and Modifying Woodworkng Tools,* 1992, Guild of Master Craftsmen Publications Ltd., Lewes, England

Klausz III, Frank, "Coves Cut on the Tablesaw"; Fine Woodworking, Sep. 1993, pp. 82-85, Taunton Press, CT

Krenov, James (1977), *The Fine Art of Cabinet-making*; Van Nostrand Reinhold, NY

McFadden, Tom, "Making a Scraper Plane"; Woodwork, June 1995, pp.38-39

Perch, David and Lee, Leonard (1981), *How to Make Wooden Planes*; Lee Valley Tools Ltd, Ottawa, Canada

Pierce, Cecil (1992), *Fifty Years a Planemaker and User;* Monmouth Press, Monmouth, ME

Rees, Jane & Mark (1993), *British Planemakers from 1800,* Third Edition; The Astragal Press

Roberts, Kenneth (1978), *Wooden Planes in 19th Century America.* Second Edition; Ken Roberts Publishing Co., Fitzwilliam, NH

Roberts, Kenneth (1983), *Wooden Planes in Nineteenth Century America, Vol.II*; Ken Roberts Publishing Co., Fitzwilliam, NH

Robinson, Monroe, "Round-Bottom Planes"; Fine Woodworking, Mar.1990, pp. 80-83, Taunton Press, CT

Rodriguez, Mario, "A Plane That's Fancy"; American Woodworker, May 1992, p. 18; Emmaus, PA

Rodriguez, Mario, "Straight Talk about Planes", Fine Woodworking, Apr. 1993, pp.67-71, Taunton Press, CT

Salaman, R.A., Dictionary of Woodworking Tools, 1975, The Astragal Press.

Sperling, Jay, & Chapin, Bert, "The Planemaker's Float"; Fine Woodworking, No. 30, 1981, p. 63, Taunton Press, CT

Thomas, William, "Building a Dovetail Plane"; Fine Woodworking, Nov.1989, pp. 54-55, Taunton Press, CT

Vandal, Norman, "How to Make a Molding Plane"; Fine Woodworking, Nov.1982, pp. 72-77, Taunton Press, CT

Weygers, Alexander, The Making of Tools, 1973, Van Nostrand Reinhold Co., New York

Whelan, John, The Wooden Plane, 1993; The Astragal Press, Mendham, NJ

Wildung, Frank, The Chronicle Vol.VIII #1 pp. 19-21 and #3, pp. 28-30, 1955; Early American Industries Ass'n., Delmar NY

SOURCES OF SUPPLY

Sources that the author has used are listed here. No representation is made that they are superior to the many others not cited.

Bench Plane Blades (Hock): The Japan Woodworker, Alameda, CA, 510-521-1810

Boxwood: Eisenbrand Inc., Torrence, CA 310-542-3576

Brass Stock: Metco Supply, Leechburg, PA 800-531-8811

Cross Vise: AMT (American Machine and Tool Co.), Royersford, PA, 800-435-8665

Ebony: Eisenbrand Inc, Torrence, CA 310-542-3576

Milling Cutters: Enco Mfg.Co., Chicago IL 800-860-3400

Planemaker's Name Stamps: Alan Davy, 1 Marina Drive, Brixham, Devon TQ5 9AZ, England

Rounders: AMT (American Machine and Tool Co.), Royersford, PA, 800-435-8665.

Screwboxes and Wood Taps: AMT (American Machine and Tool Co.), Royersford, PA. 800-435-8665.

Spokeshave Irons: Bristol Design (Tools) Ltd., 14 Perry Road, Bristol BS1 5BG, England

Tool Steel: Enco Mfg.Co.,Chicago IL 800-860-3400